Aug. 1/84

Jim

Just a wish

your wife

"Long Life"
"Good Health"
and
"Happiness Always."

Connie Blackburn

Greg Clark
& Jimmie Frise
Go Fishing

Greg Clark
& Jimmie Frise
Go
Fishing

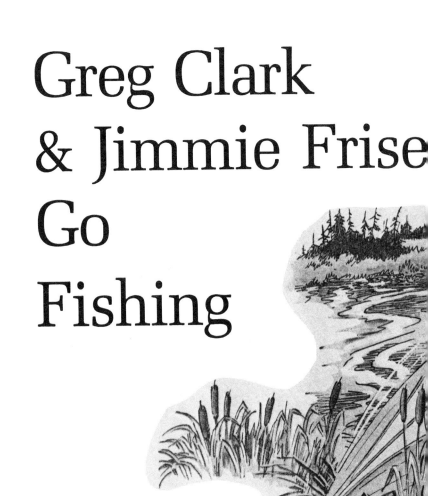

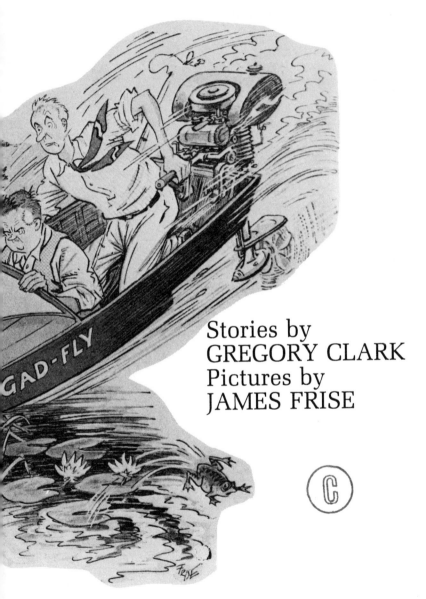

Stories by
GREGORY CLARK
Pictures by
JAMES FRISE

COLLINS • TORONTO • 1980

Greg Clark & Jimmie Frise Go Fishing
by Gregory Clark
Pictures by James Frise

This selection first published 1980
by Collins Publishers
100 Lesmill Road, Don Mills, Ontario.

The stories and pictures in this volume
were first published in the *Star Weekly*.

Canadian Cataloguing in Publication Data

Clark, Gregory, 1892-1977.

Greg Clark and Jimmie Frise go fishing

Selected stories which appeared in the Star weekly, 1930-1942.

ISBN 0-00-216618-6

1. Fishing - Anecdotes, facetiae, satire, etc.
I. Frise, James, 1891-1948.   II. Star weekly.
III. Title.

SH441.C632   799.1'2'0207   C80-094716-9

Also by
Gregory Clark
and Jimmie Frise:

THE BEST of
GREGORY CLARK
and JIMMIE FRISE

SILVER LININGS

GREGORY CLARK
and JIMMIE FRISE
OUTDOORS

The Stories

Introduction

This collection of stories is the fourth volume in a series devoted to bringing back the very best Greg Clark and Jimmie Frise stories published in the old *Star Weekly* during the 1930's.

Readers who can remember the pleasure and anticipation with which the entire country looked forward to the latest Greg and Jimmie adventure will also remember that, of all the stories, those about fishing and the out of doors were especially good. They create mood in the mind of the reader that is as relaxing and refreshing as any afternoon's fishing you'll ever find.

Like most of us today, Greg and Jimmie got through many a long week by dreaming about and planning for the weekend's outdoor adventure. And, if their plans were always perfect, reality was always full of surprises.

The warm, human quality and delightful humour that made these stories famous still reaches across almost half a century to bring pleasure to another generation.

If you remember these stories, you need no further introduction. If you are too young to have had the pleasure of fishing with Greg and Jimmie before, a whole new, wonderful world awaits you between the covers of this book. It is a world you'll enjoy and one that you'll want to share with friends.

Prominent Sportsmen

January 13, 1934

"Aw, be a sport!" said Jimmie Frise.

"I won't," I retorted. "I made up my mind ten years ago never to lend my gun again."

"Be a sport," repeated Jimmie.

"What do you mean by 'be a sport'?" I demanded. "What has sport got to do with me lending my good gun to some stranger who will abuse it, neglect it and return it to me all rusted and corroded. What's sporty about that?"

"Take a chance; be a sport," said Jimmie.

"Listen," I cried, "this sport business needs to be debunked. It's one of the oldest gags in the world and one

of the dullest. Every year, a million men are persuaded to do something against their better judgment by somebody telling them to be a sport. It's time we showed up sport. It's a racket. There's nothing sporty about it."

"Hold on," exclaimed Jimmie, shocked.

"If anything makes me mad," I went on, "it is to see a picture in the newspapers of men that have just died, and they refer to them as well-known sportsmen. All they ever did in their life was lean on the picket fence at race tracks, sit in free seats at hockey games and prize fights, gamble a few dollars on sure things that they got from somebody on the inside; and they call them prominent sportsmen. I tell you a man who takes a Pekinese for a walk after supper is a far more real sportsman than these defunct gents in derby hats."

"You're excited," said Jim.

"You bet I'm excited," I cried. "Look at us, with fifteen thousand of us sitting in the grandstand looking at fifteen men doing something like playing a game or riding race horses. And we think of ourselves proudly as sportsmen because we are sitting there. The only sportsmen are the jockeys and the players of the games."

"Would you call fishing a sport?" asked Jim.

"I fish," I said, "but I deny that anglers are sportsmen. They are the craftiest chizzliest people on earth. A true angler is one who not only would not tell his own father where the best fishing hole was, but would deliberately direct him to the wrong one!"

"Heavens!" exclaimed Jimmie.

Look At This Manly Art

"Yes," I said, "you take fighting. I don't mean boxing in the ring, for money. I mean plain fighting."

"The manly art," said Jim.

"Yes," I sneered, "the manly art! Just look at it. They set up certain rules. They make certain things foul. You aren't supposed to hit below the belt, to kick or use your knee. This they call the manly art."

"Good gracious," said Jim, "you wouldn't call a man a sport who would fight with an empty bottle."

"Just a minute, Jim," I said. "You are not thinking

clearly. You are just submitting to the old racket. These who call themselves sportsmen set up a code of fighting, and then they practise at it. They become experts in hitting and in defending themselves against blows. They then feel a great pride in themselves. A great security. They are sportsmen, and gentlemen. So they go proudly and perhaps arrogantly through life, as men do who have some advantage over other men. And suppose they pick a fight with me on the street or in a theatre lobby or at a party. I know nothing of their art. But they are experts. And they have built up a vast tradition, a whole religion, you might say, about the manly thing, the sporting thing, the gentlemanly thing. They expect me to fight them according to the code at which they are masters. They have every advantage of me. If I fight according to their code, they know they can knock the stuffing out of me. Yet they are sportsmen and gentlemen. I say they are common cowards!"

"Oh, no!" cried Jim, shocked. But he was beginning to see my point.

"Yes, sir, dirty cowards," I said. "Because, safe-guarded by their rules, which a stupid world has swallowed whole, they only need to use the muscles they have trained. If I, ignoring their code of what they even have the nerve to call British fair play, kick them on the shins or give them the knee in the soft spot, they howl about fouls and sportsmanship. That is sportsmanship in essence. Sportsmanship has fallen from its high estate to be merely a scheme whereby those who adopt the theory may have an advantage over others."

"Gosh, you're cynical," said Jim.

"I warn you and I warn everybody," I said, "that from now on I'm no sport. I won't be intimidated by any such racket. If anybody wants a fight with me, I give them fair warning of one thing. And that is, I'll fight by no artificial code. A fight is a fight, and I'll sock them with whatever is handy."

The World is Too Codified

"Has anybody been threatening you?" inquired Jimmie.

13

"No," I said. "But I'm through with codes. The world is too codified. Everything is codes, and codes are schemes for getting the advantage of the majority. Now you take manners. Take table manners. A certain group of people adopt a code of table manners. They all agree how to sit, how to hold their knives and forks; not to drink tea out of their saucers, not to leave the spoon in the cup, not to eat noisily, to pretend you are not hungry, and so forth. If you don't know their code of manners, not only are you not admitted into their sacred circle, but what is worse, they have so kidded us, that we actually feel uncomfortable in their company because we are nervous of our manners. The whole scheme of life is a system of codes for keeping the mass of mankind feeling inferior."

"Ah," said Jim. "You're feeling a little inferior to-day. That's the trouble, eh?"

"I have no trouble. All I am doing is debunking the sporting thing, the manly thing, the gentlemanly thing."

"Well, what are you going to do about it?" asked Jim. "You aren't hankering to dine with the dook of something, are you?"

"I like to eat with gusto," I said. "I don't think eating was ever intended to be a formality."

So I lent Jimmie my gun for his friend to go shooting, and I even offered to go along as chauffeur, and drive one of the cars of the party which was going up into York county to shoot jack rabbits somewhere around Aurora.

Now, I don't know whether you know it or not, but up around Aurora there is rising quite a gentry. It is becoming the Westchester County of Toronto. People live on farms all over the place, and they have a hunt club, and a kennel club, and they hold meets. Country life is coming back via Aurora. You will see people in tweeds walking about the country fields, with dogs of all descriptions, and guns under their arms. You need never be surprised, in North York, to have a man on horseback come vaulting along over the fences, a regular squire. They are even beginning to get ruddy faces, and the richer they are, the less they trim their mustaches, and the bigger their boots.

14

I don't think Jimmie or any of his rabbit hunting friends knew they were intruding on any such squirearchy as this when they headed west off Yonge St. near Aurora and the three carloads of us staggered along the rutty country roads for a mile or so, where we parked to scatter forth into the fields.

"Come and walk along with us," said Jim.

"No," I said. "I'll just sit here in the car and snooze, I'm too short in the leg to wade around in snow and mud."

Lost in York County

It is cosy sitting in a closed car on a lonely winter road with the snake fences and the homely fields leaning away wistfully. I had brought along "An Angler's Garland," and I read its verses, dreaming of the spring to come, and fishing all the pools of the imagination, as Lord Grey said. Then I fell asleep and rested in that comfortable condition until just at dark, when voices of the returning rabbit hunters waked me.

It had been snowing again, and when we got the cars loaded up with the muddy sportsmen, it took us quite a while to get under way, and then we had to take a roundabout road, because the country track was too narrow for us to turn. I was driving the last car containing Jimmie and two of his friends. We drove slowly along the rutted road. We made turns and jogs.

"Wait a minute!" cried Jimmie. "They've taken the wrong turn!"

I honked the horn. But the two cars ahead went steadily on.

"We turn here," said Jim. "It'll take us out to Yonge St. far sooner."

"We'd better stick together," I suggested.

"Turn here," said Jim.

We turned, and inside of five minutes, the road ran out. It ended in a broken rail fence. There was not a light to be seen far or wide.

"Now," I said.

"Turn her here, and go back one lot," said Jim. "I remember this road."

15

We negotiated the turn, and at another small road, with hardly any ruts even, Jim demanded we turn again. In the stormy night, because it was now really snowing, we slewed along, and took two left turns since there was no other turn.

"H'm," said Jim, when we came to what undoubtedly was a gate.

"Now where do we go?" I asked. It was supper time.

"We'll drive in here," said Jim, "and ask the farmer where we are."

He hopped out and opened the gate for me. We drove up the lane, past trees and small hills. Then lights appeared ahead and we drove into the farm yard. It was a small house, very tidy, with a big barn and stables and a hay stack looming picturesquely alongside. Several motor cars were parked in the barn yard. A whole pack of assorted dogs came rushing barking out at us.

"I'll just hop out," said Jim.

He went up to the farm house and a man appeared at the door. In the light, Jimmie could be seen talking and gesturing. The farmer came out on the snow, and Jimmie walked out to us.

"Come on in, boys," said Jim. "He wants us to come in and get warm. And have a bite to eat."

"Let's get on home," I said.

But the other two in the back seat were already clambering out with their muddy boots and leather windbreakers.

"It's one of these swell North York farmers," whispered Jim.

"You fellows are in no shape to pay a visit," I cried.

"Come on," said Jim. So the four of us walked up to the house where the farmer was waiting in the open door. From inside came a hum of gay voices, warmth and the smell of food.

One of the Most Elite Farmers

Our host was a short, fat man, middle-aged, and wearing a loud Norfolk jacket. He had on old slippers. He took our coats and hats and led us into the big room where all the excitement was.

An old fashioned farm dining room, with a hanging lamp, and big heavy furniture, and the room was filled with about fifteen people, men and women and girls.

"Folks," said the farmer, "I have brought in a few lost rabbit hunters for a bite to eat. Just make up and be friends."

Jim and his two friends in disreputable sweaters, now that their leather jackets were off, waded right into the crowd.

"It's just a buffet supper," said our host, whose name appeared to be Bill, "so help yourself, and eat hearty."

I, the only presentable person in the party, waited to be properly introduced, but Bill vanished and two men in white coats came in and started carving. On the immense sideboard were roasts of beef, cold chickens and ducks, a ham, great piles of salad, sliced bread, little dishes with funny looking things in them and at either end, a coffee urn of very old silver.

An elderly lady in a tweed suit walked over to me.

"Don't be shy," she said. "Wade right in. My name is Mildred."

And while Jim and his two shabby friends scattered over the room and sat on chair arms balancing plates of meat and salad, and Jimmie stood in the middle of an admiring crowd, telling them about the day's shooting, Mildred got me a plate and looked after me, while I stood back, very embarrassed for my friends, for undoubtedly this party we had so unceremoniously barged into was a party of very well-to-do people. By the furniture, the silver, the pictures, I concluded we had indeed got into one of those elite farms of North York.

"I'm very sorry my friends have plunged in this way," I said to Mildred. "They don't know any better."

"Oh, Bill's house is open house," said Mildred, helping me pick up my napkin which had fallen and getting me a new fork when I dropped mine.

"They are not very presentable," I said.

"Do you dress up to shoot rabbits?" asked Mildred.

"I wasn't hunting," I explained. "I was in the car."

"Ah, you're the chauffeur?" cried Mildred eagerly.

"No, madam," I said, dropping the knife and a hunk of potato salad off the plate.

I left Mildred and went over near Jim but he was having such a good time that he never saw me. I worked over near Jim's two friends, to try and get in on the groups, but there was no room. So I went over into a corner of my own and finished my meat and stood with aloof dignity while Bill, the host, galloped about, seeing everybody was fed.

Mildred, the elderly lady, had joined Jim's group.

Then one of the men in the white coats went and let the dogs in and everybody made a big fuss over the dogs that leaped all over the place, and fed them the scraps. A large police dog picked on me for his friend and pushed me about.

The Hobo Ejectus

"Here!" yelled Bill. "Get away! It's just an old custom of mine, I let the dogs in to say good-night after supper."

I got near Jim.

"Let's go," I whispered.

But Jim just gave me a funny look and went and sat down on a huge sofa with a dachshund on his lap. His two friends had paired off with pretty and stylish girls and were chatting away as if they belonged in the family.

The dogs were put out at last and the serving men cleaned everything away and then Bill turned on the radio and they all danced. More guests arrived. More dogs. Everybody had to go out in the storm with Bill while he checked over the stables to see the horses were comfy. That's what he said. Comfy.

We all ran around in the snow, that is, all but me, and somebody hit me on the back of the neck with a snowball. I got Jim aside and told him we had to go.

"Why?" said Jim. "It's only a step to Yonge St. and we'll be home in an hour. What's the hurry?"

"These aren't our kind of people," I said.

"What's the matter with them?" demanded Jim. But before I could answer him, he was chasing the dachshund around in the snow, around the hay stack and back of the barn. And we all had to go indoors again.

And while I sat in a corner, they danced and jumped around in the most childish fashion and sang songs.

And all of a sudden, Bill, the host, got into a fight. It appears somebody made a nasty remark about a horse. And the next thing, Bill and one of his guests, a tall, elderly man in evening dress, were rolling on the floor, gouging and kicking each other. Instead of stopping them, everybody started laughing and cheering, the girls jumping up on chairs, while these two elderly men bumped each other's heads on the floor and Bill, rolling near the fire place, got a hold of a piece of fire wood and started thumping his guest with it.

I interposed.

"Here," I shouted, leaping into the middle of the floor, "stand up and face each other like men!"

There was silence.

I was seized from behind, one hand on the back of my collar, the other on the seat of my pants, and I was propelled for the door. I was shoved through the door, out the hall, and out the front door. And then, whoever it was, and I still think it was Jimmie, gave me a hoist, and I landed out in the snow pile.

I picked myself up and went and sat in the car.

Music and song came from within the farm house.

Figures moved across the blinds. Cars came and cars went.

And just before midnight, along with a herd of others, Jim and his two friends came out, and we drove away.

"Well," I said, "so much for that."

"What got into you?" asked Jimmie. "You were so sulky."

"I wasn't sulky," I said. "I was just trying to act like a gentleman."

"And see what you got?" said Jim.

"What did I get?"

"You got the hobo ejectus."

"What's that?"

"The bum's rush," said Jimmie.

Which shows that the best manners are not to worry about your own or anybody else's manners.

Fisherman's Luck

May 12, 1934

The trout rose and struck. . . . "Run up to the sporting department," I said to Jim, "and get a landing net."

"How," asked Jimmie Frise, "do you like my new fishing costume?"

"Beautiful. Jimmie!" I cried.

And it was beautiful. It was a rich Donegal tweed with large patch pockets and big pleats behind his arms and down the back.

It had plus fours so baggy and so long that they hung nearly to his boottops. It had that look you see in the advertisements of the very latest English styles in the very smartest American magazines.

"Jimmie," I exclaimed, "you wouldn't go fishing in that lovely suit!"

"Why not?" demanded Jim, still turning round and round for me to see him in all his Old Country splendor.

"Why, it's for sitting on the verandas of exclusive club-houses!" I declared. "You could go to the races in it and

get your picture in the rotogravure. It is for walking about the lawns of those magnificent homes in Toronto's lastest up-the-creek suburb. That isn't a suit for going fishing. That is a sport suit."

"Isn't fishing sport?" asked Jim.

"It certainly isn't," I assured him. "Look at sport model cars, sport model clothes, well-known sportsmen and so on and you'll see what sport means. Sport means where there are a lot of people to see you. The races, baseball, horse shows. That's sport."

"What is fishing then?" inquired Jimmie, draping himself carefully on a chair.

"Fishing is a pastime," I replied.

"Then this is my new pastime suit," said Jim. "I am sick and tired of seeing people looking like tramps when they go fishing or camping. I see no reason why people should want to look dirty and shabby when they go forth to commune with Mother Nature. If we love Nature we should put on our best raiment when we enter her temples."

"That's good, Jimmie, but it isn't practical," I said.

"Why not?" demanded Jim. "These tweeds are as easy and loose as any old sweater I ever had. And these plus fours are twice as easy as any canvas pants I ever bought, badly cut and cramping your movements. And can't I drive my car and walk across meadows and wander along streamsides quite as happily in these garments as in a lot of misshapen cast-offs? Won't I feel better fishing in these clothes?"

"They'll get dirty," I said.

"There is no dirt in the country," said Jim. "It is in the city there is dirt. In the country all is clean and pure. You dust off any clean earth that might touch you. I say, save your old clothes for the city, where there is dust and soot and filth and grease. And save your good clothes for the lovely clean country."

Humble Ancestry Calls

"You certainly seem right," I admitted, "but there must be some reason back of the universal habit of putting on shabby old clothes to go fishing."

"I'll tell you what it is," said Jim. "It is the Old Adam in us. We are descendants of a long line of dirt farmers, sheep herders, peasants, peat burners, cotters, laborers, shingle splitters, and so forth. In every ship that came to Canada century ago there were, in the cabins above deck, two or three families of nervous gentry, younger sons of obscure small town politicians who had enough pull with Queen Victoria's uncles to get their bewildered offsprings jobs as surveyors, curates, town council clerks, and so forth in the colonies.

"Down in the steerage, below decks," went on Jimmie, "were some hundreds of odds and ends, starved farmers, unemployed carpenters and masons, wild young men, people who could no longer pay their rent or who were sick and tired of Napoleon and his wars and the Duke of Wellington and his peace, and who came heaving and rolling across the Atlantic to a promised land of freedom and opportunity.

"Now," said Jimmie, redraping himself on the chair, "those half a dozen nobles in the cabin above decks have multiplied enormously in the past three or four generations. And those hundreds down in the steerage have practically died out. No trace of them remains. There is not in the whole of Ontario a single descendant of the steerage. Who, were your ancestors?"

"Er—ah—" I said.

"Precisely," said Jimmie. "Your ancestors were English officers retired on half-pay and given big land grants or something? Or were they government officials sent out to help rule the illiterate colonies?"

"I wear old clothes when I go fishing," I said humbly.

"Good!" applauded Jimmie. "Good for you. An honest man. You wear old clothes when you go fishing because your humble ancestry calls to you, your humble blood begs within you to dress for a little while the way your race has dressed for ages—in homely and undistinguished garments."

"I see," I said.

"You love to put on old clothes," went on Jim, "because it gives a feeling of spiritual honesty. No more pretence. No more bluffing. There you stand, in ragged garments,

23

and all your ancestors for a thousand years, in the bogs of Ireland and on the sheep-clad hills of Scotland, salute you!"

"When I am fishing," I admitted, "I do seem to see people on the hillsides."

"However," said Jim, "I have bought this suit to go fishing in and to go rabbit shooting next fall. I am through with my ancestors."

"I would be willing to bet you," I said, "that in my old brown pants and green sweater I could catch more fish than you can in that fancy sport suit."

"Clothing," said Jim, "has nothing to do with it."

"I bet you," I repeated.

"Ha, Getting Respectable!"

"I take you," said Jim. "I wish we could go fishing right now."

"We can," I stated.

"It's the middle of the week," said Jim.

"We can go fishing right now," I insisted.

"For suckers or mud-cats in the Island lagoon?" asked Jim, with all the contempt of Donegal tweed.

"For speckled trout," said I, "one and two pounders. Fourteen to eighteen inches long!"

Jim undraped himself from his chair.

"Where?" he breathed.

"In the basement of a departmental store," I said, "right here in town."

Jim looked at me wildly.

"There is a fountain down in the glassware department in the basement of the store," I went on. "In that fountain are at least two dozen trout. Big ones."

"But we can't fish for them!" cried Jimmie.

"Who is to stop us?" I asked.

"Why, the floorwalkers, the store detectives, the salesgirls," said Jimmie, disgustedly.

"We could fish for ten minutes before anybody could make up their mind what to do," I said. "The first salesgirl to see us fishing would have to run and tell an older salesgirl. And she would have to go and find the manager of the glassware. And he might be hiding behind any one of those tall counters of glass or pottery. I judge we would have a full ten minutes."

"It sounds nutty to me," said Jim.

"See," I cried. "That's what fancy clothes do to you in fishing. It takes away your nerve. It makes you respectable."

"It isn't that," muttered Jim, who hates to be accused.

"Let's run up to my house," I said. "I'll get on my old green sweater and canvas pants. We'll use one fly. We'll toss to see who gets first cast. If the first one of us doesn't get a trout in five minutes he hands the rod to the other. I bet you I get either a bigger or more trout than you do. And I lay it all on the clothes. Because we will be using the same rod, leader and fly."

"It sounds nutty," said Jim.

"Ha, getting respectable!" I sneered.

"What will we say when they stop us?" asked Jim.

"We will say we are simply testing out a fly we had bought at the sporting goods department."

"It still sounds nutty," said Jim.

But he stood up and took his hat.

We slipped into my house and I got into my green sweater and canvas pants. I also got my old fishing hat. I got out my light fly rod, reel and line. And we drove downtown.

Fishing in the Fountain

At this season of the year it is not out of the way to see a gentleman carrying a fishing rod. We got into the basement and I led Jimmie over to the fountain, where he stood and stared with rapt joy at the pool in which some large goldfish and a few mud turtles profaned the crystal water in which lazily great olive colored trout fanned the water anxiously and felt the spring creeping through their veins. Unhappy trout, I thought, as I looked at them. Here in a pool, safe, no doubt, but so far from all the mischief and adventure of the dancing stream, the changing skies, the soft sweet loveliness of May . . .

"Ah, well," I said, "we'll be giving them a little fun in a minute."

"Sssshhh!" warned Jim.

Three ladies, four men and two children were standing about the fountain, gazing without a word at these fish lazily moving about the limpid pool. Especially the men. They were shabby men. They needed haircuts. They stood with hands behind them, with one knee bent, as if they had been, and were going to be, there forever. It would be nice, I thought, to know the thoughts that wandered in the minds of these four shabby men, standing staring so secretly at the trout, those jewels of the Madonna.

I led Jim back from the fountain and we got behind a pillar which was piled high with glassware. Nobody was around and nobody would pay any attention. I jointed the little rod and quickly threaded the line and knotted on the leader.

"Toss," I said.

Jim took a coin and tossed. "Heads," said I.

And it was heads.

I walked casually over to the fountain. Jim came behind me. I smiled two of the four men out of the way, and then I knelt beside the fountain. I whipped out the line, waved it to yet a yard or two of length, and then dropped the little greeny-gray fly fair over the nose of the biggest of the trout.

Crash! The trout rose and struck so instantly, so savagely, I had no idea how homesick he had been.

I stood up. The trout raced frantically about the pool, lashing it into a foam. The other trout raced crazily about and the goldfish fluttered excitedly about. A mud turtle became so perturbed he climbed right out of the fountain and started for the exit.

"Run up to the sporting department," I shouted to Jim, "and get a landing net!"

Old Clothes are Luckier

By this time, of course, a crowd was gathering. One of the shabby men was shouting encouragement to me in a hoarse Scottish voice. Ladies were screaming. Then I felt a hand grip my arm and the gentleman who turned me around was a stranger.

"Pardon me," I cried, "don't you see I'm busy!"

And then my line came free. A sickening sensation. The trout was off. Peace descended on the pool. But the crowd was starting to mill about for a view, as crowds will when the victim is a small man.

"My friend," I said, "will explain. We were trying out a new lot of trout flies we had got at the sporting goods."

"What friend?" said the man who had my arm.

Jimmie was standing over by the decanters, in all his tweedy magnificence.

"That gentleman over there," I said. "In the tweeds."

"Is he a friend of yours?" asked the man, looking me up and down, hat and all.

"Certainly; he is with me."

"Ha, ha," said the man. He wore a blue suit. He had a cold Irish countenance.

"Jimmie!" I called, as the man shoved me through the gathering.

But Jimmie just picked up a decanter and looked at it appraisingly, as if he had not heard me.

The man took me up to the sporting goods. Fortunately, the manager knew me. He explained to the man in blue that I was an ardent angler, a fly fisher, in fact, and that at this season of the year all anglers, but especially fly fishers, were likely to be a little touched.

I bought two dozen flies and the matter was closed. I unjointed the fly rod and went quietly back down to the basement. Jimmie was standing by the fountain, looking with interest at the trout.

"Well," I said, "I guess I win."

"I wish I had won the toss," said Jim gloomily. "Look at that trout there, the one by the corner!"

I turned cautiously and there was the large man in the blue suit, his hands behind his back, rocking on his heels and toes. He was looking straight at us and there was no expression at all in his eyes.

"Old clothes," I said to Jim, "are luckier than new clothes."

So Jim is going to save his Donegal tweeds for the races.

Don't Shoot!

October 27, 1934

"It's me," I screeched as Jimmie took aim. "And the rug! Don't shoot!"

"These bear rugs," said Jimmie Frise, "make this open job of yours a very nice little car."

"Yes," I admitted. "Considering it is four years old. But an open car is the only car for a sportsman."

We were headed out for the country on a rabbit hunt. Our friend Eddie, who owns hounds, was to meet us at one of those big swamps beyond Fergus.

"A sportsman," opined Jimmie, "has a pretty comfortable life, take it all around."

"Yet it has its dangers," I pointed out. "To the casual spectator, seeing us bowling along comfortably smothered in fur rugs, and in our snappy mackinaw clothes, it might look like a life of ease. But consider the hard work we do, the tramping for miles across fields, the struggling through dangerous swamps, and then the guns. Don't forget the guns. The dangers of carrying firearms and shooting them off, that's the peril."

"Sport is not sport," said Jim, "if it has no element of danger or risk in it."

"Is golf sport?" I asked.

"Well, you might get hit by a golf ball."

"Sport," I said, "in its truest sense, is doomed. You can't shoot live pigeons any more. As a little boy, I recall attending live bird shoots and seeing my uncle bang down a hundred pigeons without a miss as they were released from a trap. We can't enjoy that any more. Little by little, all the sturdier forms of sport are being slowly strangled. When I first went deer hunting, we could kill two deer each, and we had a month open season. Now we have twelve days to kill one, and we aren't allowed to use hounds to chase them to us."

"The world is getting more humane," said Jim.

"But all the time it is becoming more humane toward wild animals," I protested, "the more cruel the world is becoming toward men. More human beings have been shot, murdered, mangled, tortured and gassed in the past twenty-five years of the reform of sport than in the previous thousand years of stag hunting, bull baiting and cock fighting. It looks to me as if man, being denied the outlet of killing animals and birds, has turned his attention to his own species."

"You're a swell theorist," admitted Jimmie.

"A man is entitled to a little danger, a little violence," I continued. "You can't suppress it. You can't cut it out of him with a surgical instrument. Sooner or later, we are going to have to go back over the past five hundred years of reform and do it all over again by taking into account the true character of human nature."

"Well," said Jimmie, "we still have a little rabbit hunting left."

"Sure, but now you can only get a gun license from September 1 to April 30," I corrected. "And every year the farmers are putting more restrictions on us. You wait. Inside of a few years, we won't be even allowed to hunt rabbits."

Just a Few Sports Left

"We will still be able to play golf, tennis, bowls," said Jim.

"We will still be able to play those games that meet with the approval of the reformers who rule us. People," I said, driving more rapidly, "who have no hunger, no urge, no fire, no blood in themselves, and who go about enviously depriving their healthier and more natural fellows of a little action, a little excitement."

"Rabbit hunting," said Jim, "sometimes has a lot of excitement in it. I love the music of the hounds, the sight of them, all brightly colored, coming streaming through the woods or across the fields. The shooting of the rabbit is only an incident in the whole adventure. It's the chase that counts."

"I feel ashamed, every time I go rabbit hunting," said I. "When I think of my ancestors hunting stags and wild boars, bears and wolves."

"Did you get these bears?" asked Jimmie, fondling the glossy furs we were cuddled in.

"No," I admitted. "One was sent to me by a friend in the bush. The bear got its head stuck in an empty jam pail out on the garbage dump, so my friend had to put it out of its misery. The other one I bought from a gentleman who peddled it around the office."

"Very romantic, both of them," agreed Jim.

"They make a snug article to go rabbit hunting in," said I.

"They give you a sense of adventure anyway," agreed Jim, settling back and inhaling the chill October air as we skimmed northwestward toward our tryst with Eddie and his pack of rabbit hounds.

We took turns in driving, and Jim had the last lap that

31

bore us through Fergus and out some lonely autumn roads to a region of far-flung black swamps, where the bright swamp hare was numerous in his coat now changing from brown to snow white.

We met Eddie at the prearranged cross-roads. He had a small truck, the back of which is for holding the hounds. He led us down some narrow swampy roads, turning right, and then left, as he penetrated deeper and deeper into the gloomy depths of cedar and spruce. The swamp was very wet, the road treacherous, but at the end of twenty minutes we came out on a stoney pasture, lonely and bleak in the gray weather, and all we could see on all sides were vast areas of silent brooding swamp.

The hounds were crazy to be let loose. Six of them, they raced about, excited and whining, watching us set up our guns and donning our hunting coats. Then they began sniffing about the edges of the pasture, and before we had got the cars half parked in the pasture, one of them, Dainty, let loose a deep belling song and all of the six fled into the swamp with a music that has been thrilling the heart of men for thousands and thousands of years.

"Let's get going," spluttered Eddie. "You take the right side of the swamp, Jim, and you head straight in there. You'll come to a ridge, about two hundred yards in. Stay there. That's where most of the rabbits cross."

Jim went one way, Eddie the other, vanishing into the dark impenetrable cedars, so I set a true course and followed Eddie's directions. I found the ridge, a stoney mound, and there I took my stand, while far off the hounds made music.

It is lovely being alone in a swamp. The mystic silence, broken only by the tiny chirp of little autumn birds or the startled scurry of a squirrel. The sweet aromatic smell of the cedars and balsams. I picked a good spot from which I could watch in all directions, and then, gun ready across my arm, I waited for the hounds to bring the hare across my path.

But the hounds went farther and farther, until I could barely hear them, even in the silence. Now and again I would hear them coming nearer and I would get set and half raise my gun and aim it at imaginary rabbits, just to get my eye lined up. But then the music would grow faint again.

Bang! Far away, a shot. For fifteen minutes I listened intently before I heard the hounds again. This time they started less than a farm's width away, and around in a great circle they went in the other direction. I heard them grow faint and near, near and faint, and then— Bang, bang!—two more shots, followed by silence.

I yelled.

"Jimmmiiieeeee!"

But only silence answered my cry. It was chilly, so I walked up and the down the ridge. I sat down and waited. A wind had risen. No hounds, no shots disturbed the great stillness of the wind through the cedar tops.

"Hang it," I said, "is this hunting?"

So I decided to go for a little walk through the swamp and see if I could kick out a rabbit for myself, without the aid of hounds.

It is easy to go wrong in a swamp. The farther I went, the worse the swamp got. I came to a dense thicket of alders and small willows, and when I tried to go back out of it the worse it got. I came to a little stream flowing through the swamp, and I followed if for ten minutes looking for a suitable log to cross it. By the time I found the log I could see the stoney meadow through the cedars, the meadow where our cars were parked.

Some people can pop across a log as easy as walking along a pavement. I nearly always slip off. This time I slipped off and fell into the small creek. The creek was not deep, but one loses one's balance and falls. I fell lengthwise in the chill little brook and before I could regain my feet I was thoroughly soaked from head to foot.

It was not three minutes out to the meadow and the car, but I was chattering with cold when I reached it. I removed my clothes in a twinkling and threw the bear robes about me. Then I reached for my car keys.

Jimmie had them. When he got out of the car he had just popped them in his pocket.

You can't dry yourself on a bearskin lap robe. There

was nothing else in either car. And I couldn't start the car, to drive out to the last farmhouse we had passed to ask them to dry my garments at the stove.

"Boy," I said, "you'll catch pneumonia!"

I huddled under the bearskins, but they are stiff things that don't lend themselves to tucking in. Gaps are always left for wind to blow up.

I tooted the car horn, long and loud.

No answer. No hounds. No shots.

I fired two shots rapid, a signal of distress if ever there was one.

A Grand Target

A Blue Jay laughed from a hidden tree. Far away in the direction Jimmie had taken I heard the sound of an axe chopping.

"Jimmm-eeeee, hoy!" I yelled.

But the distant axe went on chopping, so I figured there was a farm at the other side of the swamp and likely Jimmie would be there conversing with the farmer or even drinking cider in the farmhouse around the kitchen stove with the folks.

I spread my garments over the hood of the car and wrapped the largest rug around me. I pulled on my soggy hunting boots and started in through the belt of swamp in the direction of the axe. It would at least keep me from dying of goose-flesh.

As I pushed through the swamp I decided to keep up a regular call:

"Don't shoot! Don't shoot!" I repeated at every step.

The swamp was deeper and wetter the way Jimmie had taken. I crossed two creeks and each time I saw a clearer place ahead, I found on arriving at it, it was only a patch of impenetrable alders.

"Don't shoot! Don't shoot!" I repeated loudly, as I came from under each cedar tree.

Every fifty yards I paused to halloo for Jim. But the silence was profound, the day was grayer and the air more chill.

"Don't shoot! Don't shoot!" I called, with monotonous regularity.

Suddenly behind me I heard a terrible sound.

It was the sharp, startled bellow and bay of a hound.

Before I could turn to look I heard other hounds join in the chorus, and in an instant I knew I was the prey of the whole pack of Eddie's hounds. There is something panic-striking about a pack of hounds on your trail. I should have simply dropped the bear rug and stood forth, in my human mastery, before the surprised hounds. But I did what rabbits do, and foxes, what Liza did with Little Eva in her clasp as she crossed the ice—I turned and ran like a rabbit.

It was all a matter of a few seconds. I could hear the hounds coming, the full terrible chorus of them, high ones and low ones, belling and baleful, a swift, inescapable choir of wild savage voices, frantic with excitement, and I did some leaps that would have credited an Olympic athlete.

Then came the shot.

Just a terrific bang amidst the cedars, and at its call I fell down. In another instant the hounds were on top of me, tearing at the rug I clutched about my shoulders.

"Help, help!" I yelled the muffled tones.

"Hold still," came Jimmie's breathless voice, "until I get him in the head!"

"It's me," I screeched. "And the rug! Don't shoot!"

So Jim ran up and kicked the hounds off and raised me to my feet.

"Thank goodness," I gasped, "you are a punk shot!"

He wrapped the rug around me and led the way out while the hounds and I slunk in confusion behind him. We drove out to the farmhouse and sat around the kitchen while my clothes were dried.

"You see," said Jim, "there's excitement even in rabbit hunting. I should say we have all the thrill in rabbit hunting any man would want!"

"Quite," said I.

Vice Versa

February 16, 1935

As I stood there, scantily clad in a bathing suit, hat and shoes, I saw Jim's feet go suddenly from under him and, with a wild yell, he plunged right into the open hole . . .

"I see by the papers," said Jimmie Frise, "that Bobbie Pearce and some of these other great oarsmen are training right in the middle of winter."

"Ah, they're tough," I agreed.

"Training," went on Jimmie, "by rowing amongst the ice cakes off Scarboro Beach.

"Do they wear coon coats?" I asked.

"No," cried Jim. "They just wear their rowing togs, short pants and a sweater. In all that ice and wind. They're tough all right."

"I imagine," I suggested, "that an athlete in good condition doesn't feel the cold the way ordinary mortals do. Their blood is fresher and quicker. There are no clinkers and dust and shavings in their blood, like there is in ours. It's a fresh, clean, hot stream and it keeps them warm."

"Besides," said Jim, "these oarsmen are so big. They are monsters. And I shouldn't think they would feel the cold as quickly as little people. Or thin people."

"You're wrong there," I pointed out. "The bigger they are the more of them there is to feel the cold with. We small people never feel the cold the way large people do. There isn't so much of us to get cold."

"Yeah, but what there is of you," argued Jim, "chills through so much sooner."

"I don't feel the cold," I assured Jim. "You never see me with a red and sniffly nose, like most people. I am compact, snug, warm."

"Then I suppose you feel the heat of summer worse than large folk?" asked Jim.

"No, because there isn't so much of me to get hot," I explained. "I haven't as much surface for the sun to beat upon."

"You're hard to beat, aren't you?" inquired Jim, but really not admiring me. "You're quite a comfortable little party, aren't you?"

"I get along," I admitted.

"I suppose you regard yourself as really being in the class of Bobbie Pearce and such chaps," pursued Jim. "It would be nothing to you to go and row a boat around amongst the ice floes of Sunnyside."

"If there were anything to be gained by it," I agreed, "I could do it well enough."

"It's a wonder you have never taken up the cult of winter bathing," said Jim. "How is it you aren't one of those super-sportsmen who drive down to the lake these mornings and go for a smart plunge through a hole cut in the ice?"

"That," I showed Jimmie, "is just so much bunk. Anybody could do that. The air, as a matter of fact, is colder than the water. As you take off your clothing, your body is first chilled by the cold air. You plunge into the water, only for an instant. And actually, the water is warmer than the air. While the crowd stands around and gapes in admiration, you really found it more comfortable in the water than in the air. Do you follow me?"

"Not into the water," assured Jim. "It must be great to have theories about everything, like you. It must make you feel pretty contented to go through life understanding everything and always ready to explain things to others."

A Simple Demonstration

"What are you hinting at, Jimmie?" I asked, sensing he was making fun of me.

"I'm not hinting," said Jim loudly. "But it makes me laugh to see a little fat guy like you sitting there with your feet on my radiator and your overcoat bunched up under you for a pillow and your hat sitting over on the edge of your head so you won't feel its weight, so blame lazy you haven't even changed position for nearly an hour, sitting there, by golly, talking about how easy it is to go bathing through the ice in winter."

"But it is," I explained. "It's simple, for the reason I have told you. The water feels warmer than the air."

"Aw, bosh," said Jimmie.

"It is easier," I stated, "and pleasanter, to go for a plunge in winter, out of cold air into warmer water, than vice versa."

"Than what?" asked Jim.

"Than vice versa," I said. "By which is meant, than in summer, diving out of warm air into cold water. Anybody will agree to that."

"I won't, for one," said Jim.

"As a matter of fact," I went on, "if it weren't for all the trouble it would take, I wouldn't think twice of going for a duck through the ice, if only to teach you a lesson."

"Listen," said Jim, "I'll take all the trouble, I'll drive you to the lake, I'll cut the hole in the ice, I'll undress you and afterward I'll dry you and dress you, if you will dive through the ice. Or even, by golly, if you'll so much as wet your big toe through the ice!"

"Jimmie," I said sadly, "it is people like you that cause all the trouble in the world. It is people like you that bring about changes of governments. You're the disturbers. You won't believe anything you are told. You've got to see for yourself."

"I've sure got to see you ice bathing," admitted Jim.

"It doesn't need proof," I assured him, taking my feet down off his radiator and stretching. "Can't you understand, my dear fellow, can't you actually feel, how much more pleasant it would be to dive out of cold air into warm or warmer water . . ."

Jim leaped up from his drawing board. He dashed to the coat rack. He started to dress in a sort of pale fury.

"No," he shouted, "I can't understand! I'm tired of talk. I hear talk on the radio. I read talk in the papers. I hear nothing but talk, talk, talk here in the office, at lunch, on the street, over the phone, everywhere. And now I'm going to see some action."

"Where are you going?" I inquired.

"I'm going down to Sunnyside," said Jim, "and you're coming with me. And I'm going to see you demonstrate a very simple, commonplace fact, to wit—that it is a pleasure to dive out of cold air into nice warm water."

"Tut, tut, Jimmie," I said, putting my feet back on the radiator. "You're primitive. The modern way of proving anything is by argument. You don't see the greatest scientists doing anything any more, do you? They just sit and think. And talk. Einstein contributed more to modern science than any man alive to-day. But does Einstein do anything? No. He just sits and thinks, writes a few words down on a piece of paper, and lo, the whole world of learning is at his feet."

Picking Warm Colors

"Get up," said Jim, coming over and standing beside me.

"Does Einstein," I asked, "have to slave around with a lot of derricks and steam engines and models of the heavenly bodies? Not him."

"Get up," said Jim, assisting me by getting a grip under my arm.

"Jimmie," I protested, "don't be ridiculous. Cutting a hole in the ice, you'd get all perspiration and then you'd catch your death of cold. Maybe you'd get pneumonia."

"Come," said Jim, helping me toward the door.

"Now, Jim, no fooling," I warned him. "We've got along very nicely the last while without any quarrels. Don't let us start now, over a trifling matter, a matter so simple that even a school child could understand it."

But Jimmie just shoved me through the door and started me along the corridor to the elevators, holding me by the back of the collar and the seat, as you might say, of my overcoat. What is professionally known as "the bum's rush."

I have long since learned that there is no use resisting Jimmie when he gets one of these forceful moods on him. I have also learned, with this and one or two other exceptions, just how far to go in conversation and debate with him, without rousing a sense of action in him. But he will stop at nothing when he starts manhandling. He has even explained, as he took me prisoner through crowded streets, that I was a poor harmless lunatic he was taking to hospital. He has also submitted me to the indignity of being carried by him as if I were a child. It is better to simply go, when he insists.

We went down in the elevator. I have every confidence in my powers of persuasion. I felt I could talk him out of any ideas he might have between The Star building and Sunnyside.

"Jim," I said, "how'd you like to come up to the Royal Ontario Museum and see the collection of wild ducks they've got."

"Duck is the word," muttered Jim, leading me up the lane toward the garage where he keeps his car. "Duck, right under. Duck your head. Duck is good."

It began to feel a little goose-fleshy.

"Jim," I went on, "I happen to know the curator of

41

birds at the museum. He would let you inside to see the great filing cabinets filled with ducks."

"Duck," gritted Jim. "Duck right under the water. That'll keep your mouth shut."

Brrrrr, I thought.

We got into Jim's car in the garage. At the repair shop, Jim got out and borrowed several items, an axe, a shovel, and a sort of long handled cold chisel.

"I have no bathing suit," I said.

"I'll get you a bathing suit," muttered Jim. "And it won't be any fur bathing suit."

"I refuse," I stated, "to go in without a bathing suit. It wouldn't be decent."

Passing the canoe club, Jim stopped and got out and went inside. I had my chance. I could have got out and run and hid. But before I could decide, out came Jim with a red bathing suit with blue and white stripes.

"I picked the warmest colored one I could find," said he, getting in behind the wheel.

"You're Responsible For This"

We drove along toward the Humber. I could feel myself growing smaller and smaller. As we passed by, a train puffed out of the Sunnyside station, its huge engine looking hot and steamy in the frigid air.

"Have you any preference," asked Jim, "as to where you would like to dive in?"

"Jimmie," I said, "this has gone far enough."

"If you don't dive in," said he, "I'm going to throw you in."

"One thing," I said, "you'll have to cut a good big hole. I don't want to dive into any little two by four hole and get caught under the ice."

"I'll make it," said Jim, reassuringly, "as big as you want it."

"I want a hole about six feet square," I pointed out. "That means a lot of digging. Maybe you would prefer to do all that work to-morrow?"

"Six feet by six," said Jim. "I can chisel that through in twenty minutes easy, while you are undressing in the car."

He drove to the Humber and then down on to the lake shore beach. It was terribly rough with ice and humps and floes that had been washed ashore.

"It's a foot thick," I protested. "You'll never get a hole dug by dark."

"If you'd prefer," said Jim, "to walk out to the edge there and slide off?"

"I want you there to help me out," I replied.

"Then," said he, "it's a hole. How will this place do?"

He stopped the car and got out, with his shovel and axe and long-handled chisel.

"Don't try to run," he said, tossing the bathing suit on to my lap. "I'll catch you if you do."

"You're responsible for all this," I stated, as he slammed the door.

I watched him pick a place out on the ice. I saw him trying the ice in various places. Then he started to work, throwing off his overcoat and wielding the axe.

He chopped and chiselled and the chips of ice flew and then he stood up and signalled to me.

I started to undress.

The car was cold, bitter cold, and I took my time so far; and then hurried. I got the bathing suit on and my overcoat atop of it and my shoes on my feet when I saw Jim walking off the ice toward the car.

"Come along," he said, holding the door open.

He held my arm as we walked down to the beach.

"You're not fooling?" I asked him.

"Vice versa," said he.

He had a hole chopped about six feet square. It was full of chips and slush. A few large chunks bobbed about in the gray soup.

"Clear out those hunks," I said, "and a lot of that slush. I don't want to dive on to a rock below."

Jimmie squatted down with the shovel and started scooping out the slush. The big hunks were slippery and he had a lot of trouble with them. I stood huddled in the coat.

"Vuh-vuh-vuh-vuh!" I shivered.

"The colder you get," said Jimmie, "the warmer the water will feel. Am I right?"

I nodded.

"All right," he said, standing up and surveying the pool now clear and green and almost clear of slush. "Get your coat off."

I removed my coat. I stood with my hat on and my boots.

"All right," commanded Jim.

"Jimmie," I said, as a last resort.

He started to walk around the hole toward me. He took two impatient strides. He stepped on a smooth place he himself had made, shovelling out slush.

And before my horrified gaze, his feet went from under him, he seemed to leap into the air, and with a wild and awful yell, he plunged, in a sitting posture, right into the open hole.

He splashed me. I retreated. The water seemed to burn, like molten metal.

Up he came, hat first. He was already blue. He flung his arms out on the ice and his fingers moved feebly, as if beckoning me.

I crept as near as I dared, and held out to him the shovel. Painfully, he heaved. Painfully I pulled. Slowly he slid out of the hold on to the ice.

"Jimmie," I cried, "whatever did you do that for?"

I got my overcoat around him, to keep the wet off me, and then I held him up while we staggered in a kind of run for the car.

In the car we tore off his boots, coat, clothes. I helped wrap him in the rug and my coat, although it was very messy work, with all the water off him dripping icy cold around the seat and floor.

He never said a word. He just kept on gasping.

"Now wasn't," I asked as I rubbed him, "the water warmer than the air? Didn't you find that the air, on coming out of the hole, was colder than the water? Isn't it a fact that the immersion in the water was not anything like as unpleasant as you thought it would be?"

He just glared at me dully and signalled for me to get

44

at the wheel and drive.

"Or," I asked, "was it vice versa?"

But he looked so terrible, I just climbed into the driving seat and drove him home.

Mmmm, Mmmmm

February 29, 1936

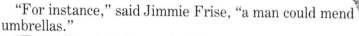

"For instance," said Jimmie Frise, "a man could mend umbrellas."

"True, Jimmie," I mused. "When I was a boy, I recollect the umbrella menders. There would be one come along our street at least once a month. They would have a half a dozen tattered old umbrellas under their arms, and a little bag of tools, like a doctor."

"They would rap at each door," went on Jim, "and say to the lady, with a lift of the hat, 'Any umbrellas to mend, lady?' "

"Nowadays, I still see scissors grinders," I confessed, "with a little treadle strapped on their backs, and ringing a hand bell through the streets."

"They are foreigners now," said Jim. "But when I was a boy, they used to be our fellow countrymen. And the children would come and gather round to see the blue sparks fly off the wheel, and to hear him sing. I knew one Irishman, a young Irishman, with a bright face, and he loved sharpening scissors and knives. And he used to sing a tune in time with his foot pumping on the treadle.

"Let me see," said Jim. *"Where does this wheel go?"*

A quick tune."

"I can't understand a man nowadays," I stated, "being out of work. There are so many things a man can do. Things men used to do, that seem to be forgotten. Why, I remember the spectacle sellers. Don't you remember the spectacle sellers? Nicely dressed young men who, when you opened the door, were standing there, with a bright smile, and a sort of suit case strapped around their necks and spread open in front of them filled with spectacles of all sorts fastened to the tray. From door to door, these merchants went, fitting spectacles to all the housewives."

"And," cried Jimmie, "the packmen! With a big black oilcloth pack on their backs and a tray in their hands, containing everything the home required—needles, threads, buttons, tape, elastic, bobbins, wool of all shades, hooks and eyes, buckles."

"I remember," I admitted, "my dear old grandmother searching all over the house one time for a bodkin, and finally saying—'I wish the packman would come by.' And then she stopped still and looked wistfully out of the window, and said 'Why, I haven't seen a packman in thirty years.' And that day, she grew many years older."

"The packmen," said Jim. "Merchants, with their stores on their backs. To-day, if a man comes to your door with needles, thread, shoe laces, all he has got is a little bit of stuff in his hands and he is so shabby and importunate, you know he is only begging. But packmen never begged. They were proud men. They were merchants. Merchants of a prouder and older order than these modern ones that sit in stores. They belonged to that ancient craft of merchants who travelled by camel train and little ship across all the earth, selling as they went."

"I've got three of them," I remarked.

"Isn't that a funny thing?" mused Jim. "I have, up till this minute, thought of those clocks just as ornaments. It is years since they went. I wonder why I haven't done anything about them?"

"Because," I stated, "the clock menders no longer call from door to door. Because you can't think of anybody to come and take them away. Because they are too big and clumsy to take downtown yourself. I beg there is a million dollars' worth of clock mending to be done right in this city."

"I wonder," thought Jimmie, "if it is because we have all grown lazy and indifferent? I wonder if, as the result of all the invention of the past fifty years, life hasn't become so soft, so easy, that the whole human species has grown lazy, careless, indifferent. Why wouldn't I go to the trouble of taking a clock off the mantel, carry it out to my car in the morning and deliver it to a store downtown?"

"Nobody wants to do the little old-fashioned things any more," Jim went on. "Even the piano tuners. Do you remember the piano tuners? You didn't have to send for the piano tuner. He just turned up."

"I remember, even," I submitted, "a sort of general mender that used to come around about once a year. He had a wooden box on his back. He used to sit in the vestibule. He could resole shoes, mend leather gloves, sew up carpets that were torn, mend carpet sweepers, regild picture frames . . ."

"Unemployed!" scoffed Jim, suddenly jumping up. "No work! What is the world coming to? The country is full of work, if people would only wake up and realize it. And the grandest kind of work of all—working for one's self."

"I guess the only kind of work anybody wants now," I said, "is what somebody else tells them to do."

"Well," stated Jim, "one good thing has come out of this conversation. I'm going to get my clocks repaired."

"The same here," I said. "Only, it seems a shame that after all this talk about laziness and loss of enterprise, I have to confess that I am the great-grandson of a clock-maker."

"Are you?" said Jim.

"Yes, my great-grandfather, born here in York, before it was Toronto, even, was Thomas Bradshaw McMurray, watchmaker, probably the first native born watchmaker in this city."

"Indeed," said Jim. "Maybe some of these countless clocks that aren't going all over Toronto were actually made by him."

"Possibly," I confessed. "But I inherit not the slightest aptitude with machinery of any kind."

"You would hardly call a clock machinery," pointed out Jim. "A clock is, after all, a very simple mechanism. It is, in fact, as simple as a child's wind-up toy. It consists of a spring you wind up, a ratchet that holds the spring, and a series of geared wheels which relax the spring at a rate controlled by levers with tension on them. Really very simple."

"Even so," I confessed, "I have a horror of opening a clock. I must inherit some reaction from my great-grand-father. I shudder even when I take the back off my wrist watch. To look in and see all those tiny, delicate wheels and sprockets and springs breathing, as it were. Breathing and slowly ticking, ticking, like the beat of a heart. It gives me the creeps."

"You surprise me," said Jim. 'All I see to clock mending, is, unscrew the works, take it all apart, laying each separate piece in a precise spot on the dining room table, so that you will remember just when, rather than where, it goes back. Wipe everything with a rag dipped in gasoline or some such solvent. Re-oil with great care, and very sparingly; and then re-assemble. I should think it would be very simple."

"Jim," I cried. "Don't do it. Don't you do it."

"Besides," went on Jim, "if we learn how to mend a clock, then anybody can learn. And we could then not only advocate clock mending as a trade to the unemployed, but we could actually, when some poor chap calls at our door with a packet of needles or soap, bring him in, teach him the trick of clock mending in an hour or two, and set him on his way a free man, a man with a trade and calling."

"Mmm, mmm," I said, doubtfully.

"How about the country?" demanded Jim. "You pass all these little villages and cross roads in the country. There is no glazier there, but all the windows are mended. There is no clockmaker, no plumber, no tinsmith, no dentist, but all the country's clocks are ticking in the kitchens, the pumps work, the roofs are tight . . . there must be men all over this country who do know about making things go."

"Give it up, Jim," I begged him.

But Jim went back to work at his drawing board with a hard dry look in his eyes, and that night, when the telephone rang right after dinner, I knew it would be Jim, and it was. And he invited me to walk three doors south to his place to see him mend a clock. And of course, a man would be a pretty poor specimen that wouldn't do that much for a friend.

The clock, which Jim had standing on the bare dining room table, was a large greenish yellow marble clock with gold pillars at the corners and a gold ornament on top. It was a clock made after the shape of a post office or the British royal exchange or maybe the Greek temple of Thought or something severe. Jim had the dining room doors closed and locked.

"I have here," he said, "the small screw-driver from the sewing machine, a large screw-driver, a thing to tap with, in case of rust, a rag moistened with gasoline and an oil can. The whole outfit wouldn't cost a dollar."

Jim removed the back of the clock with four deft twiddles of the screw-driver. He peered inside, studied, examined, lit matches and peeked, and finally undid a large screw which let him lift out the bowels of the whole clock. It was heavy, brassy and compact.

"I will start at this corner of the table," explained Jimmie, "and work across the table diagonally that way. I will lay each thing I take out, in its proper order. Thus, when reassembling the clock, I will start at that far corner. And so, as simple as falling off a log, it will go together again."

I said nothing. Beads of unseasonable perspiration began to stud my brow.

Jim removed eleven screws, large and small and laid them, in a sort of row, across the table. Then removed the whole disjointed carcase forward to the head of the row, and delicately pulling, lifting, twisting, he began to take the machinery apart. Each piece he laid separately in the row.

"See," he said, breathing heavily, "how simple it will be?"

I just moaned.

He worked straight across the table and then made a wide turn and started back on a second row. Still the machine came apart. Still grew that incredible line of parts, wheels, screws, levers, bolts. The spring came away, a thick, dreadful looking thing, coiled like a serpent. Jim studied it, looked through its coils.

"Just as I thought," he said. "Gummed with ancient oil. Glued, you might say. I will swish it in a bowl of gasoline."

But on, on he went, finishing the second row and starting on a third. The face of the clock fell out. Jim picked it up and detached the hands.

"There," he cried. "Was that difficult? Was that intricate?"

I stifled a groan.

With his gasoliney rag, Jim proceeded to wipe each part. He rubbed and scrubbed.

"Be careful," I said hoarsely. "Don't lean against the table. Don't jiggle the least bit."

"Imagine a man," remarked Jim, "having a horror of clock insides!"

"It's inherited," I muttered.

And then Jim, shifting the duster in his hands to get a fresh clean bit to use, flicked with the tail of the rag the middle row of parts. It was just the lightest possible flick. But my rivetted and fascinated gaze saw a small brass wheel and a very tiny steel pin about the size of a one-inch nail, scamper across the table, and I let out a yell.

"You've ruined it, you've ruined it!" I shouted.

But Jim, bending down, picked up the wheel and the bolt and a sort of rocking-beam sort of thing like on the top of an old-fashioned steamboat. It had a hole at each end.

"Not that, not that," I hissed.

"I remember where they go," said Jim easily, and he bent over, studying the rows of parts, and looking for the space the parts belonged to. "Here, this is where the wheel was. Or was it the rod?"

"I'm going home," I stated.

"Just a second," exclaimed Jim. "Let's see. This flat thing was here. And this wheel was . . . there. Was it?"

"Oh, oh, oh," I moaned.

"Mmmmm," said Jim. "I remember this large sprocket was there. It must have moved too. I'll put it back there, and then this . . . Let's see. This . . . Well, well, mmm, mmm, dear me."

He straightened up. He stared narrowly at the rows of bits.

"Jim," I said, taking his hand tenderly, "I'm off. Good-night."

"Hold on, a jiffy," said Jim, eagerly. "Now, wait a minute."

But he was frightened, and it showed. There was perspiration along the top of his forehead, too. I couldn't leave the poor chap in such a plight. I hid my face in my hands and sat down.

"Mmm, mmm," Jimmie kept saying. "Mmm, mmm."

I heard little clicks. I heard snaps, clinks, snucks and taps. I heard things going together and things being grunted apart. I heard a loud tapping, and looked up to see Jim hammering a wheel onto an axle, using the butt end of a screw-driver.

"It's all over," I said brokenly.

"Well, anyway," sighed Jim, holding a small gear about the size of a dime, "I've found one thing I've been looking for for months. This gear will exactly fit my casting reel. The one with the black handles."

"Please," I begged, "don't start trying to tinker with your fishing reel."

"It's the very fit," said Jim. "And now I know where I can get wheels and springs and anything like that."

And he laid the clock on its back and rescrewed the face on it, and then laid it on its face and in its back door he just dumped, dumped all the works, packing them in and prying them in with the screw-driver and tamping them down with the butt of the screw-driver, and finally getting the back door closed and the little button turned.

"There," he said. "Nobody will ever notice."

"Not until spring cleaning, anyway," I pointed out.

"And that's away off in May," said Jim cheerily.

Groundhogs

July 18, 1936

"Groundhogs," said Jimmie Frise, "are at their best right now."

"For eating?" I begged.

"For shooting," said Jim. "The fields are deep with grain or clover. The groundhogs have lost that anxious alertness of the spring. Fat and free, they sit on their little mounds. They make a perfect target."

"A target, eh?" I asked.

"An animated target," said Jim. "The mind of man can't discover any other use for a groundhog. Their meat is too soft. Their fur is sleazy and thin. The divine purpose of a groundhog, as far as I can figure, is to provide an animated target for farm boys and city sportsmen in the off-season."

"Hmmm," said I.

"The bad points of a groundhog are well known," said Jim. "They not only eat crops, such as winter wheat, clover and so forth. I've known farmers to have their entire crop of Brussels sprouts ruined by groundhogs.

"I started to dig out the hole into which the groundhog Jim had shot at had dived . . ."

But in addition to their damage to crops, groundhogs cause a lot of damage to horses. Horses step in groundhog holes and break their legs."

"The survival of the fittest," I explained. "Nature realizes that the horse has numerous and powerful friends, while the groundhog has none."

"As a matter of fact," said Jim, "I can't figure out why Nature ever invented a groundhog. It has no earthly use."

"Nature," I stated, "didn't figure the way man was going to steal the show when she did her designing. She simply set loose a lot of guesses. Nature is a gambler. She doped out a few hundred designs and then sat back and said go to it."

"Wouldn't it have been swell if the groundhogs had won?" jeered Jimmie.

"I can't think of any life more agreeable than a groundhogs," I admitted. "They have no economic value, therefore they are not enslaved like the cow and the horse and dog. Their fur is valueless, therefore they have not met the fate of the beaver and the fox. Their meat is of no interest, therefore they are not hunted as deer are."

"Thank heaven," said Jim, "for the sporting instinct of humanity, or the entire face of the earth would now be pitted with groundhog holes."

"A groundhog," I continued, "has a delightful life. Unlike the fox and the raccoon, he lives in a dugout of his own building, safe from life's war. A nice warm dugout, with two or three entrances in case of danger. On his fast little legs he can jump into one of his dugout entrances at the first sign of hawk or human. He is a wise baby who digs his home in the midst of human endeavor. He selects a nice clover or grain field, and makes himself a home where he won't have to move more than ten jumps from any one of his strategic entrances."

"They're stupid," said Jim. "They sit erect like fools, right on the doorsill of their burrows, a perfect target."

"In time," I countered, "the groundhogs will learn that they can't take any chances with men. The more groundhogs learn about us humans, the more they will develop long range rifles and telescope sights. So that in time, no groundhog will ever sit up at the door of his burrow. That is Nature's way. Don't think men are entitled to win in this gamble of Nature. Sooner or later, one of the other contestants in the race will get the bulge on us. And believe me, it will be a bulge."

Winter Doesn't Bother Him

"Do you mean," demanded Jimmie, "that groundhogs might some day conquer the human race?"

"Why not?" I inquired. "Just because we humans have been top dogs for a few million years recently is no reason to suppose that Nature's gamble is ended. The way men have been behaving lately, I'm willing to put a bet on the beetles at any reasonable odds."

"Beetles!" ughed Jim. "Make it groundhogs."

"Think," I said, "of the way groundhogs hibernate during the winter. There is real civilization. There is genuine economy. A groundhog, when the time comes, simply goes down into the deepest depth of his dugout, curls up, draws a few pebbles and handfuls of sand around him, and goes to sleep. Not for him are the hardships and rigors of winter. Not for him are starvation wages. He simply goes to sleep and spends all the winter months dreaming idly of the pleasures of summer. Then when spring comes, he wakes, and finds his winter dreams true, new shoots of grain growing, and life ready to amuse and feed him. Don't you wish we humans had thought of hibernation about two hundred million years ago?"

"It would have been an idea," agreed Jim. "No doubt Nature missed several good bets in connection with men, and hibernating was one of them. And wings was another. And a sting was another. I often wish I had a great big sting like a bee's. But all the same, you haven't mentioned any good reason for groundhogs. I don't see why we shouldn't consider them as just something to shoot at."

"No doubt, you're quite right," I confessed. "Judged by the same standards, a great many human beings cut no more figure in this life than so many groundhogs. They might be regarded as something to shoot at."

"The only difference is that the groundhogs can't complain to the authorities. They can't get even," said Jim.

So when Wednesday, Jim's half day off, came along and he signalled me to follow him from the office, I did so, and we walked down to the parking lot, and in Jim's car was his rifle and several boxes of shells. And it being a lovely day and the birds likely to be mad with love and song, I went along, mostly to see the birds. Jim said that south of Georgetown were some wonderful sandy and gravel hills just lousy with groundhogs, and that way we went. And long before we spotted the first groundhog I was well paid by a no less beautiful sight than two cuckoos flying with their curious snakelike motion, and a Blackburnian warbler and no end of commoner birds which are to me like people I know as I pass along, and so life is less lonely.

Up a hill waving with green clover, and against a beautiful old boulder fence, we spied our first groundhog. He was all unaware, busily feeding, and not until we were within about forty yards of him did he suddenly sit up, the picture of indignation, his dark brows making him look very like an indignant fat man disturbed in his rightful business.

We lay down. Jim put the rifle to his shoulder and drew a careful bead. He drew and drew, breathing heavily and then holding his breath, and finally he touched off the trigger.

There was a loud plunk.

"Got him," cried Jim, leaping up and racing towards the fence. But I saw the little brown beast scamper furiously and vanish into his hole in a sandy knoll of his own building.

"You only winged him," I accused, as I ran alongside. "He got down his hole."

"We'll find him lying dead just inside the entrance," said Jim.

But when we got to the little mound, and found the dark and secret entrance to the cave, there was no groundhog sprawled at the gate, nor was there any sign of blood.

"I heard it go plunk," said Jim.

"Listen," I commanded.

And from out the hole in the ground came, as from a

distance of several feet, a faint squealing sound. It was
a sound like newborn puppies make, and it was inter-
spersed with a snapping or chopping sound which groundhogs make with their teeth as a warning.

"Jim," I declared hotly, "there are babies in this den."

"It's the one I hit," said Jim. "Squealing its last."

"Pardon me," I said, "but that is baby groundhogs
making that squeaking sound."

In the pleasant afternoon, soft with light and tend-
erness and joy and the love that broods in summer, we
stood listening and then we knelt and finally we lay down
with our ears at the hole.

"Suppose," I accused, "that you have killed the mother
of a brood of baby groundhogs?"

"Let's go and find another," said Jim, getting up.

"Jim, I'm going to dig these out," I stated. "I'm going
to go to that farm we passed back there and borrow a
spade."

"Listen," said Jim, "why be a silly sentimentalist?
Groundhogs are vermin. Why don't you do something
about all the beautiful baby sheep and baby pigs that are
being slaughtered every day at the packing houses?"

"Wait till I come back with a shovel," I commanded.

It was only a couple of fields back and the lady at the
farmhouse gladly gave me a shovel.

"For groundhogs?" she said. "I hope you dig them all
out."

Jim was asleep on the mound when I got back. He said
he would stand guard over the other exits of the groundhog burrow while I dug.

"It isn't likely more than three or four feet down," I
assured him. "And anyway, I want to show you what
you have done."

At first I intended to dig out the burrow the way drain
menders dig out a sewer pipe, that is, by making a ditch
that reaches down to it. But the entrance penetrated
straight down for about five feet and then slowly sloped
deeper still, and by the time I had burrowed six feet, I
was under the stone fence and Jim was squatted at the
entrance of the tunnel, watching me.

"Make it bigger," he said, "so I can come down."

"Go get a board off a fence," I directed, "and come half way in and scoop the dirt back out as I dig."

Ahead I could still hear the faint squealing of small animals, and this served to excite me on. Jim returned with a board and kneeling on knees and hands, he skited the earth I dug back between his hind legs like a terrier. We began to make progress.

The tunnel straightened out and ran like a gallery ahead. All I had to do was cut the earth around the hole already made by the groundhog and pass it back.

"Look," I cried, "here's a branch tunnel leading off. Isn't this smart? Just like a German dugout in France."

Something stabbed me on the knee.

"Jim," I cautioned, "be careful with that plank."

"It isn't near you," said Jim, skiting sand.

"Ouch," I said, "what the dickens are you doing?"

Something whistled sharply, and a heavy furry object like a bag of something soft such as flour, struck me violently in the pinnie.

"Back, Jim," I shouted loudly. "Back."

"What is it?" asked Jim, not backing, but leaning forward as if to see in the dark over my shoulder.

By now, there was a scuffling and a scurrying, a whistling and a chunnying, a teeth-grating and a scratching; with a dexterous movement, I let Jim follow his curiosity while I heaved past him, and left him in rear. In the darkness, there was a sense of danger and of menace.

"Look out," cried Jim in his turn, pushing at me to make way. "They're attacking us."

And with Jim assisting me, I made good time up the tunnel and we burst into the blessed wide open spaces with sand in our hair and grit in our teeth. We backed a respectable twelve feet from the hole we had made and stared down.

"For heaven's sake," said Jim, "the little brutes actually attacked us."

From the shadows far at the bottom of our excavation there rose a chorus of menacing sounds, curious hoarse whistles and grindings, chucky grunts and snappings. Like a jack in the box, a brindled fat figure popped out a foot and then instantly back. It repeated this bold manoeuvre three or four times while Jim and I stared ready for instant flight.

"I'll be jiggered," I said. "The little savages."

So I stooped and grasped a boley, which is a pebble egg-sized or up.

"Easy," cautioned Jim. "Don't irritate them. We've only got a little twenty-two."

He picked his rifle up gingerly, and held it behind him.

"In the case of bears," I suggested in an undertone, "they say the best thing to do is walk quietly away. Don't run."

"Come on, then," agreed Jim anxiously, for the sounds in the cavern were increasing, as if groundhogs were gathering from all the subterranean passages for miles around to man this pass of Thermopylae.

We backed slowly. We did not remove our eyes from the excavation. No fierce sabre-toothed groundhog head showed. We turned. We walked smartly. We ran. We got into the car and slammed the doors and rolled up the windows. Jim held the twenty-two on his knees.

"Ah," we said.

"That's gratitude for you," I said. "Me trying to do a noble and humane deed, and they attack us."

"You can carry humanitarianism too far," said Jim. "Sometimes, humanitarianism is against the laws of life."

"The ungrateful little brutes," said I, bitterly.

"To tell you the truth," said Jim, "I was afraid they might have rabies. That's why I didn't want to let them near me."

"It was the shock that made me hurry," I explained. "Shock and rage at their ingratitude. The vermin."

Jim rolled down one of the car windows and stuck the twenty-two out. No fanged heads showed above the sand-pile high up against the stone fence.

"Just fire one," I said, "to show our contempt."

So Jim fired one, and the little spurt of sand showed he had hit the fortifications.

"Yah," I yelled. "Take that."

So we drove back around through Georgetown and all the pretty little towns and scorned groundhogs from then on.

61

Without A Paddle

August 1, 1936

The little boat leaped the lily pads and struck a grassy island . . .

"Rest," sighed Jimmie Frise, "oh, to rest."

"It's nice here," I remarked.

"Yes, but listen," said Jim, raising his head from the hammock. "Listen to those cars whizzing past on the road

back there behind the cottage. Listen to those motor boats."

"They make a nice drowsy sound," I pointed out.

"Listen to that radio next door," groaned Jim.

"It's playing Fats Waller," I announced. "Nice stuff."

"Speed, speed," said Jim, tragically. "I am surrounded, hemmed in, smothered, strangled, suffocated by speed. How can I rest, when every sound and every sight around me is a sound of dreadful speed?"

"Just relax," I said, "like me."

"Do you know," said Jim, "I haven't had a real rest since about 1908?"

"What happened then?"

"I left the farm," said Jim. "Ambition bit me. I up and left the farm. And by golly, I have never had a decent rest since then."

"What do you call rest?" I inquired drowsily. I was on the couch on the veranda.

"Well, on the farm," said Jim, "there were a lot of ways of resting. You could rest at night, when you went to bed about eight o'clock."

"Country time," I agreed.

"The roosters, cows, pigs and horses waked you," went on Jim, happily, "with their mooing, squealing, crowing, kicking and stamping. So you got up around five o'clock. Standard time."

"Were you glad to get up?" I asked.

"Yes, because you knew you were going to get lots of rest," said Jim. "So you did your chores. Then you came in and had a nice little breakfast. I've often eaten corn on the cob for breakfast."

"How extraordinary," I muttered.

"It's a cereal," explained Jim. "And I've often eaten pie for breakfast. Mince pie."

"Ugh," I said.

"Then," said Jim, waking up and taking a more restful position in the hammock, "then you would start for the barn. Some days, you would get to the barn. But most days, you would see something before you got to the barn. Maybe it would be a new hole in the chicken wire run. Or something shining on the ground. Maybe it would be a bolt. Off something, like an implement. Or you might see a hen duck under a bush. So you would go over to see if she was setting on a nest. Anyway, you would go over to see about whatever it was."

"I feel like taking a rest already," I agreed.

"It's dreadfully hard," said Jim, "in agriculture, to get to the barn."

Ah, That was Restful!

"Supposing you did get to the barn," I asked, heavily, "what would you do?"

"I never could figure that out," said Jim. "Sometimes, I would have a vague idea that I would clean out a stall or two. Or perhaps comb a horse. Or maybe back out a harrow and do a couple of turns around the plow. But it wasn't the arriving at the barn that used to interest me. It was the getting to the barn."

"Go on, go on," I said, lifting my eyelids as if they were box lids.

"Well, supposing it was a clucking hen," said Jim, "a black hen sitting on a nest of nine white eggs under a bush."

"Right," I agreed. "I have it."

"You had to sit down and consider it, didn't you?" demanded Jim, argumentatively. "You had to first peep under the bush, and you had to sit down to do that. Then you liked the look of the hen, all indignant and fluffed up, sort of. With her head on the side. And her beak slightly open."

"You used to see lots of hens," I pointed out.

"Yes, but a clucking hen," said Jim, dreamily. "There was something so interesting about a clucking hen. So you would sit there and think about her. And about the nine eggs. And first thing you knew, you were wondering about all this vast multiplication of life; how many hens there were in the world; how many clucking hens sitting on nests in China and Omaha and Surrey and Russia and Valparaiso. Ah, that was restful."

"But you could think of all that in two minutes," I indicated.

"Not a farmer," said Jim. "A farmer likes to think

slowly and carefully. He doesn't like to jump at any con-
clusions, even about Valparaiso or Surrey. So I would
sit there, resting and thinking slowly. And the hen would
blink her eyes every now and then. A hen has sort of
white rims around her eyes. She blinks hard. She blinks
as if she was always astonished."

"Please go on," I begged. "You have me all cramped
up sitting by that bush."

"Now the point is," said Jim, "all the time I am sitting
there, looking at that hen, there is nothing to disturb
me. No cars whizzing by. No aeroplanes zooming around.
Maybe a windmill the other side of the barn might give
a few squeaks and groans, flap around a couple of times
and then quit. Maybe a calf would get frisky all of a
sudden and gallop five or six jumps around the pasture.
But it would get over it as suddenly as it started, and
quiet all down again. Maybe a horse would stamp once
in the stable. Maybe a chipmunk would scuttle along the
bottom of the fence. But in all the lovely wide world, not
a thing would stir, not a sight, not a sound, would disturb
me, lying there on my elbow, secret, alone, happy, se-
rene, looking at that black clucking hen. Rest. Pure,
sweet rest."

"I would hate to ask you," I said, "what about that bolt
you saw shining on the ground, as you tried to start to
walk to the barn."

"Ah, that would take too long," agreed Jim, "far too
long; going over, standing looking down at the bolt, shining there in the dusty lane; first thinking all about where
it might have come from. Then you stoop and pick it up
and walk over to lean on the fence to think about what
you could do with it; where it would fit. No. That is a
long story. I have known a bolt like that to keep me from
getting to the barn a whole morning.

Mr. Murphy's Sea Flea

"There are people," I said, "who would die of such an
existence."

"What puzzles me," said Jim, "is why people live so
rackety a life when they can live that other quiet kind
of a life. Why do people deliberately choose to come into

cities, buy motor cars, ride on street cars, rush and dash and sweat all over the lot, when all they have to do is go out to the country, put on an old pair of overalls and a couple of boots they don't even have to lace up, and just relax?"

"We are getting somewhere," I explained, "we city people."

"Where?" asked Jim, closing his eyes.

So I closed my eyes and we just thought for quite a little while until a man selling blueberries by the basket came and disturbed us, wanting to know if we required any blueberries.

"I wish the kids hadn't taken the boat," said Jim, sitting dejectedly sideways in the hammock and wishing he had the couch instead. "We could go out for a couple of hours' fishing before supper."

"I thought it was rest you wanted," I reminded him. "If the kids hadn't taken the boat, they would have been banging and thumping around here all afternoon."

"We could walk around to Murphy's," said Jim, "and rent a boat. Let's do that."

"It's nice just lying here," I submitted.

"A fine way to spend a week-end," said Jim. "Lying on a veranda. We could have done this in the back yard at home, and saved ourselves a 300-mile drive."

"Who'll row?" I inquired.

"I'll row out, you row back," said Jim.

So he helped me up and we slippered around the cottage, getting drinks of ice water and gathering up a little tackle and stopping to look at the pictures tacked to the walls to see if we remembered what they were after fifteen years. And we walked down the balsam-lined shore road where no cars are allowed until we came to Murphy's boat house. Mr. Murphy was asleep, but his wife waked him up and he said he had no rowboats in, at the minute, and no canoes. But he would be glad to let us have the outboard.

"Outboards are my meat," agreed Jim.

"Not that sea flea, Mr. Murphy?" I said anxiously.

"It's all I have," said he. "Mr. Frise knows how to run it."

"Not me," I protested. "A belly-whacker. Nothing doing. I was in a sea flea back in 1923 and I said I would never do it again."

"Tut, tut," laughed Jim. "This is going to be fun. I didn't know you rented this baby of yours, Mr. Murphy?"

"I don't," said Murphy, "but I wouldn't see you gents disappointed, and besides I see you with your outboard, Mr. Frise, so I figure you know about them."

"I've owned a dozen of them," said Jim. "What's this horse-power?"

"Twenty-two," said Mr. Murphy. "It's a racing motor. It's really about a 30 horse-power."

"Nothing doing," I said, picking up my fishing tackle. "Imagine 30 horses pulling a little salad plate of a boat like that."

That Racing Button

"Listen," laughed Jim, lowering his tackle box down into the absurd little skimming dish, "we only use two horse-power of it, eh, Mr. Murphy?"

"Turn her low," said Mr. Murphy. "You can throttle her down to no speed at all, that baby."

"Jim," I said, earnestly, "we can't fish out of a thing like that."

"Oh, yes, you can," said Mr. Murphy, untying the mooring ropes. "Many's the fish I've caught out of that rig."

The manly thing is to assert your principles, but when you are stampeded, it is hard to do the manly thing for fear they would think you were scared. So I got in.

"I filled her up not an hour ago," said Mr. Murphy. "Give her a twist and throttle her down."

Jim wrapped the rope around the big flywheel, and gave it a lazy spin. The engine burst into a furious explosion, fumes leaped and whirled, and the little dish skidded out. Jim instantly throttled her down and with a kind of double-action, the sea flea began to move across the water.

"Watch out for that racing button," yelled Mr. Murphy, cupping his hands.

"Watch out for the racing button," I yelled to Jim

beside me. We were squatted on the bottom of the absurd craft, Jim at the engine, I forward, keeping her nose low.

Gracefully, we sped out on to the lake. I looked back. Jim was nose-up in the cool breeze and he gave the thing a little more gas.

"Easy," I yelled. "Keep her just about like that."

Jim nodded delightedly.

We steered for a rocky point a mile across the lake where we might pick up a few bass feeding towards evening.

"Better than rowing," called Jim.

"I thought you were the bird that hated speed," I laughed back at him.

"Okay," said Jim, turning, and fumbling with the red and black rubber buttons.

"No, no," I shouted. "I said, I thought . . ."

Suddenly, the engine gave a snarl and I felt the sea flea surge beneath me and nearly stand on its tail. I grabbed the bow and hung on, and managed to get my face turned to see Jimmie. He was twisted around, frantically twiddling buttons and shifting levers, and behind him rose up a vast white billow of foam. The water was racing past at dizzy speed.

"Watch your steering," I shouted, kicking back at him.

Jim craned his neck and I saw a queer expression on his face, a look of exultation.

"Slow it, slow it," I roared.

But Jim was craning his head to see over the high-lifted snout of the sea flea. He motioned me to get my weight forward, so I clutched up and finally assumed a sitting posture as near the bow as I could, which depressed the nose enough for Jim to see where we were heading as well as to renew his efforts to find the button for turning off this dreadful speed.

"Turn off the gas," I roared, perilously turning my head half around. Already we were passing the rocky point where we had intended to fish. In a great rushing curve we passed the point and Jim steered for the open lake.

"Switch off the ignition," I bellowed, "turn off the gas. Do anything."

The water, right under me, slid by with loud spanks, and we commenced to leap from wave to wave.

I got my head screwed around to see Jimmie still twisting this and pushing that.

"Jimmie," I roared, until he looked at me over the dreadful snarl and thunder of the engine, smoking and billowing behind us, "Jimmie, it must be the racing button. Turn off everything."

"I have," Jim shouted back. "Everything's turned off. But she still goes."

I resumed my front-face and watched the waves jumping past at sickening speed. Around in a wide circle Jim steered, and presently we were on the second lap of the lake, passing the stoney point.

"What are you going to do?" I shouted, each word by itself.

"She'll run down," replied Jim, "Enjoy yourself."

Grimly I gripped the cockpit edges of the silly little boat. I tried closing my eyes. I tried looking at the sky. But always they returned, fascinated, to that gray green blur of water slashing and leaping and spanking furiously past us.

Around one more in a large mile circle we roared, senselessly racing. What is the use of such speed? You cannot raise your eyes to see the scenery; and if you did, it was gone before you had a decent look at it. What place on earth is so important that you have to get there with such fury?

Jim steered for Murphy's boathouse, in case the engine might think it was going home and so stop itself. But in a violent twist we had to turn away from Murphy's and steer for the lake again. Still once more Jim held her in a wide circular course, until we were spanking and rocking over our own swells made ten minutes before.

"Jimmie," I bellowed, "tilt the engine up."

He tried to tilt the engine so as to bring the propeller to the surface, but all this did was depress the nose of the pie plate and give me a sheet of cold water in my lap over the snubby bow.

So he let her howl and steered for yet another grand tour of the lake at blurry speed.

"Run her into weeds," I roared. "Weeds. They'll slow her up."

North of the rock point was a bay which ended in lily pads and thick copper water weeds and bulrushes. Into this jungle of water, where large pike hid, the most powerful engine in the country could not force its way without being brought to something near a stop.

Jim steered for the weeds.

I saw the lily pads swim viciously toward us. I saw them snap past. I felt a couple of lurches, as the engine bit into the jungle of coppery water weeds. I felt it give a heave, as if it had struck a log. With undiminished speed, it leaped a final thick green carpet of lily pads, struck a grassy island and with a last furious plunge hurled us all deep on to a jelly, a quagmire, a swamp of foul black mud.

With a hiss, the engine stopped.

"So," I said, turning carefully around, "you're the bird that hates speed."

"Get the paddle," said Jim, "and let's get her out of this. We may have wrecked the prop."

"There is no paddle," I announced, after a brief look.

And there was no paddle, nor any pole nor stick. And after taking off my pants and feeling for a foothold and finding nothing but bottomless bog, I scrambled hastily back into the sea flea and put my pants on again.

"Jim," I said, "there isn't a human in sight."

And at seven o'clock the mosquitoes came out, in clouds, and at eight o'clock, our voices, even in duet, could no longer be heard a half mile. And at ten o'clock, when we heard a plain common motor boat and voices, we lighted our last matches and Mr. Murphy located us and threw us a rope, and with the engine up-tilted, we were hauled into fresh water to explain to Mr. Murphy how we had got where we were.

"Anyway," said Jim, as he showed me to my room with a candle, "one thing I've resisted having in this cottage is electric light."

"You're just an old-fashioned man," I said, bidding him good night.

Poachers

August 8, 1936

They looked our beautiful fish over. "What should we do with these two poachers?" asked one. "The police court is too good for them!"

"Contary," said Jimmie Frise, "to the general belief, speckled trout fishing is better right now, in the depths of summer, than it is in May."

"I like bass fishing at this time of the year," I said.

"And muskies," said Jim. "And pike. And pickerel. And sun fish. And rock bass."

"And chub. And shiners," I added.

"The speckled trout," explained Jim, "when the heat of summer comes on, leave their scattered and various hide-outs in the stream and congregate in the large spring holes and cold pools. It is no trick at all to catch big lunkers of speckled trout in summer."

"It is kind of unsporting, don't you think," I suggested, "to take advantage of the trout when they are all ganged up like that?"

"Well, after all, a trout is a trout," said Jim. "And if you can think of anything more beautiful, on a hot summer evening, than an ice-cold speckled trout fresh out of the water, all beautiful in his olive and blue and red and orange and white—he is getting ready for his nuptial season in October. He is beginning to dress up in his wedding colors. No bird, no creature, is lovelier than a speckled trout in August."

"A good fat twelve-incher, in May," I said, "after the long winter, when you haven't much to look at—that is pretty nice. A good fat twelve-incher, in your landing net. And you up to your middle in a dark and swollen trout stream."

"In May," retorted Jim, "they are not fat, but slab-sided, after the winter. They have not much color. But ah, later in the summer. Fat, glistening, cold, curved there in your landing net. Let me picture it to you."

"I was planning to go bass fishing," I protested.

"We'll say," said Jim, "that it is about eight o'clock in the evening, daylight saving time. The sun has sunk below the trees. The sky is still bright, with light clouds catching the radiance of the evening."

"Birds," I reminded him.

"The birds are singing, the swallows are rising and curving over the trout stream," said Jim. "High lush grass along the stream side. A long quiet pool. And we are crouched amidst the tall grass and bayberry bushes, watching the placid surface of that pool!"

"Moon," I suggested.

"The moon," said Jim, "is just a silver shaving in the sky. As we crouch there, watching the water and the air over the water, to see if we can identify any little mayfly hovering, there is a sudden swirl in the pool."

"How big?" I suggested.

"A swirl," said Jim, "about the size of a wash basin. Our hearts contract. We breathe with difficulty. We estimate, from the size of the swirl, that this trout we are about to catch, will go a pound and a half."

74

Master of the Pool

"I love catching a trout like this," I said. "We are so certain of it."

"So," said Jim, "we toss for first cast. You win."

"Thank you, Jimmie, you are a prince."

"So you rise in the long grass. You examine your nine-foot leader, tapered to four X. Fine as a human hair. To that tapered end, you tie on a pale mayfly female, of the J. W. Dunne series. It is a large yellow gray fly, with a translucent body made of artificial silk, olive-colored, and so like the real mayfly's body that you could almost eat it yourself."

"Ah, Jimmie, I am breathless," I said.

"High above the placid pool," said Jim, "your line curves, until you have just the right amount of line out. Suddenly your line checks over the water. The pale mayfly female hovers for an instant and then falls, as light as thistle down, on to the quiet face of the pool. Precisely over the very spot where we had seen the huge boil of the big trout."

"Hurry," I commanded.

"Never hurry," said Jim, "in dry fly fishing. Your fly does not sink. Anointed with oil, as it is, it floats. Lightly, on the tips of its yellow gray hackles, it floats on the surface of the pool. Like a tired mayfly, it floats motionless on the surface of the pool. A slight current carries it slowly down toward the foot of the pool, a foot, two feet. Suddenly . . ."

"Mmmfff," I said.

"Suddenly," cried Jim, "the quiet surface of the pool is burst; where your floating fly had rested, a white cascade explodes; a gleaming object, trimmed in orange and green and pure white, curves darkly amidst the white jewels of the water; your arm moves; the line tightens; your delicate fly rod arches; you struggle to your feet—you are into the master of the pool."

"Do I get him?" I shouted.

"Easily, easily," warned Jim. "Don't rush him. Don't crowd him, on that fragile leader. It is tapered to four X. Its farthest end is as thin as a human hair. Yes, you get him; after ten minutes of fury, while the placid pool is threshed and torpedoed and waved by the beautiful fish. I come to stand beside you on the pool's edge, I open the landing net. I submerge it under the water. You lead the monster carefully, exhausted, on his side, over the net. I lift. And deposit at your feet, in the long lush grass, in the shadows of evening, a trout such as you dream about; a trout fat and plump and olive and orange and white; a trout, my friend, of one pound twelve and three-quarters ounces weight.

Destiny is Destiny

"Jimmie," I sighed, "that was one of the nicest fish I ever caught."

"All right," said Jim, "how about bass fishing."

"Bass fishing," I snorted. "Bass fishing. Flinging wooden clothes pegs around at the water and hauling in big scaley mud brown fish."

"It is hardly sporting to take advantage of a speckled trout in the middle of summer," suggested Jim. "When he is ganged up with his brethren in a spring pool."

"We have only so long to live, Jim," I stated. "Both we and the trout. Destiny is destiny. If a fish is fated to be caught, he is going to be caught. Either by us or by some unappreciative country boy. I say we go trout fishing."

"I have it all arranged," said Jim. "There is a stream up in Grey county where I used to fish 20 years ago. It is a stream that never fails, even in the hottest summer. It rises in a series of huge boiling springs, and flows down through cedar swamps, interspaced by open grass meadows, where there are large bends and pools at every bend. In those pools there are springs. In those springs there are trout."

"Maybe it's leased up," I offered.

"It won't all be leased up," said Jim. "Down in the cedar swamps it won't be leased up anyway. It is too tough for anybody but the heartiest anglers. Only true fishermen would struggle through a cedar swamp."

"I can't imagine anything cooler than a cedar swamp in August," I said.

And without more ado, as they used to say, we packed

and went. Twenty years is a long time for a trout stream to survive, in Grey county. Twenty years has seen an ever increasing army of men and women bitten with the fishing bug. And they have leased up most, if not all, of the few remaining waters where the speckled trout survive. And when Jim and I arrived at the lower stretches of this lovely cold water, we saw it liberally plastered with wooden and canvas signs, warning off trespassers and poachers. We stopped at various places and got out and examined the stream. How beautiful is a stream flowing full and clear and eager, in a quenching summer month. This one was all that a stream should be, golden gravel in which we could see the little tubular cases of the caddis flies, and any amount of small creatures, insects and shells and miniature crawfish, to feed a host of trout.

But in all our journey upstream, dipping in side roads to find a spot not posted against us, we saw no angler.

"See?" said Jim. "Everybody quits fishing at this time of year."

Up and up we drove in roads growing meaner and rougher, until we came to a country of cedar swamps.

"Pick a more open section," I suggested, "we can't fly fish here. It is too dense for a fly rod."

But farther up, we came to signs again warning us off; and wherever it was open, there were signs.

"It sure is posted," said Jim. "I guess the only thing we can do is go back to the bit there by the cliff."

We turned the car in a lonely farm entrance and drove back to the swamp. We tried various places easy of access but wherever there was access there was a sign.

"Down the cliff for us," decreed Jim.

And we drove back to the cliff, parked the car off the road, unloaded our tackle and descended the limestone declivity. It was hard going. But good fishing is rarely found where the going is easy.

Fly casting was out of the question, once we got down into the swamp. There wasn't a ten foot space in which to swing a fly rod. But we dibbled our flies down under the dark and secret cedars, into eddying pools as cold as ice, under over-arching logs. The very first pool, Jim snaked out a pound fish using a wet Gordon. We crouched amidst the fragrant trees, and worshipped the beauty. The next pool was mine and I drew an eleven-incher, using a wet Grizzley King. If no time at all, in less than fifty yards of that twisting, full-flowing ice-cold stream, Jim and I each had a half a dozen trout, the biggest ones well over the pound, the smallest almost a foot long.

"Jim," I sighed, as we rested in one of the dark grottoes of the swamp, "I would gladly surrender all other fishing for this kind. Let's lay them out and have another look at them."

Which we did, and how royal they seemed on the moss, how plump and covered with a kind of golden sheen which you rarely see on trout except in the purest of water.

"With a small spinner ahead of my fly," said Jim, "I believe I could catch a two pounder. I think I have seen bigger ones whirling and curving in those holes, when my fly floated down."

So we put on spinners, tiny little twinkles of gold plate, ahead of the trout flies, and let them run down the current into the deep pools.

Jim hooked a beauty, like the one he promised me in the day dream; and I was busy getting the net under it when a voice broke into our silence.

"What are you boys doing here?"

It was a lanky gent, with a moustache, and he had the accusing eye of a game warden or a water bailiff, at least.

Most Embarrassing

I finished netting the fish and laid it on the moss and we then faced our interrupter.

"What is it to you?" I demanded.

"This here," said the stranger, menacingly, "is private water. Leased water. It belongs to a club. You're poachers."

"Like the devil we are," said Jim indignantly. "We are very respectable anglers, club members ourselves. We would never think of poaching."

"How did you get in here without seeing our signs?" sneered the stranger.

"Down that cliff right there," said Jim. "There isn't a sign anywhere along there."

"Down the cliff," scoffed the stranger. "Come sneaking down the cliff. Why of course we don't put signs on the tops of cliffs. You two gents come along with me. Come on. Make it snappy, too."

"Come along where? What's the idea? I tell you, there were no signs where we came in," Jim and I both protested.

"I'll carry the fish," said the warden, grimly, seizing our creels. "And if you make any trouble, I'll deal with you."

"Take the fish," said Jim. "And we'll go and get our car and go home. Where are you thinking of taking us?"

"To the club," said the warden, with a kind of suppressed eagerness and determination.

"Listen, brother," I said, "it will be most embarrassing for us, for reasons you wouldn't understand. Take the fish. Take our tackle. We'll pay cash to you for the trouble we have caused. But we didn't know this was posted. Who would post a swamp?"

"You come along," said the warden, menacingly.

So we came along. A little way through the swamp we found a path. The path led to an open meadow and at the foot of the meadow, by a long pool in the stream, was a cottage.

"The club house," said the warden, grimly.

On the club house veranda were several elderly and mostly largish and fattish gentlemen playing cards in their underwear and socks. Some of them needed shaves. Others looked very seedy, as if they had been playing cards for quite a long spell.

They watched with astonishment our arrival. They stood up and stared in silent and resentful amazement, as the warden opened our baskets and solemnly laid out our beautiful catch on the steps.

They looked at one another grimly.

"Gentlemen," said one of the poker players, the angriest one, "as president, I ask you what we should do to these two poachers? Is the police court too good for them? Or what?"

"I never saw a better catch," said one of the members, hefting the largest trout.

An Eminently Fair Solution

"Personally," said the president, laying his cards down, "I like to take home a few fish with me when I come up here. I suggest we send these two scoundrels back into the swamp. Make them fish. Then, if they catch enough for all of us—how many do each of you want, boys?—we will let them go with a warning."

"Sir," I said, "an eminently fair solution."

"Silence," said the president grimly. "How many do each of you wish? Name your catch."

So the members all spoke up, some wanted ten, some only wanted five; but it totalled forty fish Jimmie and I had to catch by sundown.

"The warden," said the president, "will go and sit in your car to make sure you don't try to escape. Catch forty fish, the like of these, bring them back to the club. And you may go free. Otherwise! . . ."

Jimmi and I were escorted back to the swamp. We had a glorious afternoon and evening. With spinner and fly, changing from Grizzley to Par Belle and from Par Belle to Rogue, we took forty divine fish in less than half a mile of swamp.

"Gentlemen," said the president, when we laid out our offering on the steps, and the members, now shaved and dressed for home, started dividing them up into bundles, "gentlemen, it is now customary for me to present you with a ticket each entitling you to one day's free fishing on our club water."

He handed Jim and me each a small card.

"The warden here will honor them if you present them to his house yonder," said the president. "You see, we are now a little elderly, we members. We find it pleasant to fish in the earlier season when the trout are scattered all along our property. But in the summer, when they get into the swamp, it is a little too exhausting for us.

"So," he said, "we remove the sign from the road up by the cliff. It is astonishing how it works. We never fail to get some poachers. Ed here, the warden, sits in the brush and waits. Along come the poachers. After they have proven to Ed's satisfaction that they are real fishermen, he arrests them and we then make them the proposition we made you. If they are indifferent fishermen, Ed just throws them off the property."

"Well, I'll be . . . ," said Jim and I, looking at our cards of invitation.

"Now, gentlemen, come in," said the president, "and partake of such refreshment as is left, although I regret to say we have reached the age in this club when there is rarely any refreshment ever left."

And all the members with their fine catch of trout under their arms, in newspaper bundles, came in and toasted us:

"To two very handy anglers," they said.

And they drove us by road back around to our car and left us with all pleasantness and heartiness.

"There is something," said Jim, "to human nature after all."

Dead Eye

February 20, 1937

It took me only two rounds to discover that what a man needs, even a very famous marksman, is practice.

"Have you noticed," asked Jimmie Frise, "these new shooting galleries around?"

"Don't tell me," I cried, "that shooting is coming back."

"It is," said Jim, "and with a bang. All over the country these little shooting galleries are opening up. You shoot for a pool."

"Money?" I inquired sharply.

"Cash," agreed Jim. "A certain amount of what everybody pays for his shots goes into a pot, like in poker. The target is a very tricky one. It is the capital letter Z. With three shots, you have to obliterate all the letter Z, which is in red ink on the target. If the slightest trace of red remains, after your three shots, you lose. Only the most expert marksmen, and the luckiest marksmen, can cut out all that Z with three shots from a little .22 rifle."

"Does the pot get very big?" I asked.

"I've heard of it growing to $60," said Jim. "Often it goes as high as $20."

"By George," I assured him, "that's worth shooting for."

"And very exciting, too," said Jim. "These little shooting galleries are located in shops and stores; and in their front windows they stick up signs or a blackboard and announce the size of the pool every hour or so. When the word spreads that the pool is growing big, the boys gather from far and wide to take a shot for the big money."

"And the greater the excitement," I supposed, "the bigger the pool grows, because nervousness and excitement spoils the shooting."

"I heard of a case down in one western Ontario town," said Jim, "where an old Black Watch sergeant-major, one of those regular old soldiers, used to wait until the pool got up around twenty bucks, and then he'd walk in and collect. He has carried off eight or nine of these big pools, I'm told."

"I can picture that," I laughed. "A Scotsman, cool and practical. And an old soldier. And he just walks in, very calm and coldblooded, and shoots that twenty bucks right into his Caledonian pocket."

"Certain of the bigwigs in the country," said Jimmie, "look with disfavor on these shooting galleries. They are trying to find out how they can be stopped."

"Why?" I demanded. "Don't they want the plain people to have any fun?"

"Well, for instance," said Jim, "old Colonel Lundy-Lane or some other patriot, sees in these shooting galleries a nefarious plan by which the Reds are getting in their target practice. And then Mr. Bulger Baggs, that widely known public pest, who watches the morals of the nation, hates to see anybody making $20 as easily as by shooting. If you let people make money easily, what will happen to the nation's supply of hard workers? And anyway, Mr. Baggs is no good at shooting, himself, or he'd be down collecting those twenties."

"Jim," I said, "if public opinion in the persons of our prominent patriots and well known wealthy moral guiders is going against these shooting galleries, we had better get busy."

"As Good As in My Pocket"

"Would you come with me and try a hand at it?" asked Jim.

"The money is as good as in my pocket right now, Jim," I assured him. "You've never seen me really shooting. Do you realize, if I had cared to follow it, I would have been one of the greatest Bisley shots in history?"

"I've been hunting with you," said Jim.

"Ah, yes, hunting," I protested. "I admit that at hunting I am no great shakes. But that is no test. You take a little man like me, working in an office fifty weeks of the year, and then suddenly going out into the wilds to clamber about on rocks and through swamps, carrying a great big eight-pound high-power rifle. No wonder I can't hit anything. And anyway, the muzzle blast and kick of those big rifles."

"Now I come to think of it," said Jim, "in twenty years I have never seen you hit anything."

"Jim," I informed him, "I'm not one to talk about myself and my exploits, but did you ever know I have shot at Hythe, which is the greatest musketry range in the world? Do you know that all the time I was in the army, I was conniving, every time my regiment was out of the line, to get the job of musketry officer? That I seized every opportunity that presented itself in a period of three years to shoot at the ranges? That I have fired tens of thousands of rounds?"

"But did you hit anything?" asked Jim.

"My boy," I advised him, "there is all the difference in the world between range shooting and field shooting. Some of the greatest hunting shots in the owrld are no good at all at targets. And some of the greatest target shots couldn't hit game with the flat side of a shovel."

"Are you any good with the .22 rifle?" asked Jim.

"I'll show you whether I am any good or not," I informed him, "when we go to lunch. Are there any of these shooting galleries handy?"

"There's one a couple of blocks over," said Jim. "I looked in yesterday. The pot was around $8 at that time. And there were about fifteen guys lined up to shoot for it."

"Jim," I said, "in the army, my men called me Bull Clark, because of the way I used to shoot nothing but bull's-eyes. At all ranges from one hundred yards up."

"Maybe," said Jim, "you took up target shooting in self-defence. Bull Clark, eh?"

"That's what they called me," I reminisced tenderly. "In the dark, as I would come along the trenches amongst my merry men, and they wouldn't notice me on account of my size, I would hear them talking about me. 'Wait,' they'd say, 'until the little Bull comes along.' And that sort of thing, all very affectionate. Oh, they knew a good shot when they saw one."

"Likely they did," agreed Jim.

"Of course," I related, "an officer is not supposed to do much shooting in the trenches. He leaves that to his men, and spends his time in administration."

"Down in dugouts," helped Jim.

"Well," I explained, "you daren't show any lights in the trenches, and an officer has to spend a good deal of his time down in dugouts, reading orders and looking at maps and that sort of thing, by the light of a candle.

"It all seems very reasonable to me," said Jim.

Firing At the Little Z

"But often," I went on, "my men used to plead with me to take shots in the trenches, when good targets offered. I recall one time they called me up out of the dugout in great excitement and pointed to a dark figure standing out in No Man's Land. Even in the dark, I could see it was a German. The boys thrust a rifle into my hands and begged me to fire. But just in time I recollected the traditions of the British army and, instead of shooting, I ordered my men to line the parapet and open fire on the German. They just burst out laughing, because it was a dummy they had put up for my amusement."

"Still," said Jimmie, "if you had shot, you'd have hit it, don't you think?"

"To tell the truth," I confessed, "I have trained my mind and eye to the nice perfections of shooting at a range, with the result that both in hunting and in war I am a little at sea when it comes to what you might call rough and ready shooting. But with a prize of $20 up, I feel sure my former talents will come to the fore again."

"In the artillery," said Jim, "we really had no practice at what might be called shooting. It was more like arithmetic. There we'd be, in the mud, with our gun, its nozzle pointing off into space. Three miles away, over a couple of hills, would be the enemy. So we'd sit down with a piece of paper and do some figuring. We'd add and subtract, then we'd multiply and divide. And thus we would get a number. Then we'd walk over to the gun and twiddle some dials around until we got that number, or one near it. We would all strip to the waist and then fire six shells furiously at that number. Then we'd sit down and wait. If we didn't get any messages from our own infantry that we were hitting them, we knew we were hitting the enemy. And from then on, all we did was shoot so many shells off in the morning and so many in the evening, and everybody was happy."

"You don't know what shooting is," I informed him.

So at noon, after lunch, we strolled around to the new style shooting gallery which was in a formerly vacant dry goods shop. At the rear, sheet steel backdrops served to catch the bullets fired. The range was only ten feet, and you fire standing from the off-hand position, not resting your rifle on anything. But the target was so tiny, a sheet of paper with the Z to be cut out with three .22 bullets only if they were placed with supreme accuracy one on the top bar, one on the diagonal and one on the bottom bar of the letter. You could win cigars by shooting at other and easier targets. But it was the Z that was attracting most customers. Each one who missed increased the size of the prize.

And the pot was $9.75.

We watched the boys for some time before our turn came. They seemed to be pretty good. The rifles were regular little .22 repeaters, and after each three shots, the attendant changed the card and put up a new Z. Plenty of times, those marksmen would cut the top and bottom bar, but their third shot would go wild. Perhaps with nervousness.

"Maybe the rifles are phoney," I suggested to Jim.

"No," he said, "they're good enough to shoot right on the good shots."

"Maybe every third cartridge," I said, "is defective?"

"No, it's the human element that provides the trick," said Jim. "Watch."

The shooters set themselves in fancy stances. Took curious holds and grips on the little rifle. Some held it lightly as a feather. Others wrapped themselves around it, as if they were trying to climb up it. Some fired almost the instant the sights fell on the tiny target. Others aimed and held their breath and aimed and held breath until you were fit to scream with the delay.

But none of them cut the little Z clean. There were a couple of arguments, when near complete obliterations were achieved. But in each case a tiny bit of the red letter was visible.

Jim stepped up. He fired four rounds of three. I felt

sorry for him. He went at it so like the artillery. He thought he was firing shrapnel.

"Strip down to your waist, Jim," I recommended, when, in three rounds, he had not even hit the Z anywhere. On his fourth round, he hit the top of the Z. But his next two shots were two inches off.

"Here," he said. "Let's see what you can do, Bull."

But it takes time to get the hang of a rifle again, and of a strange rifle. I may say it only took me two rounds to discover that what a man needs, even a very famous marksman, is practice.

"Well, Bull," said Jimmy as we hurried out to make room for new shooters, "you didn't do so good."

"I wasn't trying," I said. "Jim, I'll tell you what let's do. That big cellar of yours is perfect. I'll borrow my son's .22 and we can spend a few evenings brushing up. A little practice is all I need. And then we can go back in there and clean it up. Boy, did you see that pot when we left? It was $14.25. That would buy a lot of trout flies."

Practice in the Cellar

So after supper, Jimmie and I repaired to his big cellar den, where he has the pool table and the paintings of Old Archie and the Town Constable on the walls, in various sporting activities such as crap shooting and cock fighting, and we set up a rifle range. Jim had some sheet iron, and we nailed up a sort of protecting wall of boards, to the back of which the sheet iron was tacked; and we then proceeded to work. We shut all doors to keep the crack of the little rifle from disturbing the neighbors, and made red, white and blue targets of a suitable size for a range of 25 feet.

I soon showed Jimmie what shooting was. Jimmie showed me, too. We made series of bulls until we reduced the target to a mere patch in order to make it a sporting proposition.

"Why couldn't we shoot like this at noon?" I demanded.

"Well, for one thing," said Jim, "we're leaning on the billiard table; and besides, we're using stronger ammunition; these are what they call 'long rifle'. They'll knock a cow over."

"Let's try some fancy shooting," I suggested. "Just making bulls is too tame."

So we tried off-hand shooting, that is, firing without a rest. At this, we were not quite so hot. Next, we tried firing five rounds rapid. We would fill the magazine with five shells, and then fire as fast as possible to see how many bulls we could get. We didn't get so many. In fact, some of our shots were a foot or more off the target.

"I tell you," I exclaimed, "we could practise snap shots. We could turn our back to the target, and then when the other fellow calls fire, we wheel around and fire at the target point blank."

This was great fun. Some of our shots were on the target, but most of them were off on the planks to the side.

I was taking my third turn at snap shooting and fired a specially quick one when there came a dreadful crash from the cellar room next door.

"The fruit," said Jim, rushing for the door.

As he opened the door, a cloud of smoke billowed into the room.

"The furnace," shouted Jim.

And in an instant all was confusion, as Jimmie and I rushed about opening windows and doors. We inspected the fruit cellar and found that a bullet had struck a quart of peaches, bursting it and causing it to topple several bottles of cherries, plums and marmalade to the floor in transit.

On inspecting the furnace, we discovered seventeen bullet holes in the pipes, through which little spouts of smoke and fumes were leaping.

"I guess you didn't put enough thicknesses of planks and sheet iron to stop the bullets," I explained.

"Thank goodness you hit the fruit," said Jim, "or else we might have gone on shooting the furnace up and smothered us."

But even so, we had scarcely time to get the furnace pipe plugged with putty and the house aired and the fruit cellar mopped up before the family got home.

"It's just one of those things," Jimmie called laughingly up the cellar stairs in answer to inquiries. "We were just trying a little off-hand target shooting."

"It's a boy's game," I remarked when he came back into the room.

"You said it, Bull," agreed Jimmie.

Sublimation

February 27, 1937

"... the very instant I took hold, the first of Jim's three bowls came rolling back home ... and smacked my fingers cruelly."

"Every man," said Jimmie Frise, "needs some sort of winter recreation."

"Winter," I protested, "is the season for rest and recuperation. Bears and groundhogs hibernate. Birds fly away to the soft and sultry south."

"I think winter," said Jim, "is responsible for most of the world's ills. Winter provides too much time for men to brood. It is in winter you hear of all the political troubles."

"Look at it the other way," I pointed out. "Winter obliges men to spend more time indoors, talking and thinking. It is the season of annual review. Men sit about together, reflecting on the past year, the business, the affairs, life in general. I should say that in winter, the real progress of humanity has been made."

"It is in action," said Jim, "that men are happy. Only when men stop to think are they unhappy."

"Winter," I reminded him, "is the social season. It is the season of parties, gatherings, meetings, lectures, concerts. All the best movies are held over until winter. The great radio programs are reserved for winter. Summer is for the body. Winter is for the mind and soul."

"Well," said Jimmie, "it is only the wintry countries where they have any troubles. Look at Russia and Germany and Mongolia. You take the countries where they have summer all the time.

"Like Mexico," I jeered, "and Abyssinia and Spain and the South American republics."

"In those countries," said Jim, doggedly, "the heat causes men to lie around and brood and talk, the way winter does with us. What I am getting at, the less time there is for moping and talking, the happier everybody is. They talk about the coming age of leisure. The great day, almost at hand, when the mass of mankind will have only a little work to do and all the time in the world for leisure, play, reading, idling. I tell you, it will be a dread day. It will be the end of us."

"How?" I demanded.

"The devil will find mischief," stated Jim, "for idle hands to do."

"That proverb," I assured him, "was invented by some employer of child labor, some sweat shop operator, some slave driver."

"I still wish," sighed Jim heavily, "that there was something we could do with ourselves in winter, besides sitting around."

"No more skiing," I warned. "No pool rooms, no dancing lessons or anything."

"Thousands of our fellow men," said Jim, "stay happy all winter with some sort of activity, some kind of recreation. Like bowling."

"Bowling," I said. "Heaving huge balls at wooden pins. Creating havoc. Wrecking. Smashing."

"It's a swell game," declared Jimmie. "Thousands of women are playing it now, too."

"From the point of view of the psychologist." I informed him, "it is a good game. It lets off steam. It sublimates our inner cravings to smash things up."

"Phewy," said Jim, "on psychology."

Going Wild Respectably

"The ideal of civilization," I elucidated, "is that all mankind shall be tame. But there is still a little of the wild animal left in us all, even in the least expected of us. If we suppress this wildness, if we pen it up, it is going to cause us trouble, inside: in our minds and spirits. Bowling, alley bowling, allows us to go a little wild respectably."

"You have an explanation of everything, haven't you?" said Jim.

"That's because I sit around in the winter, thinking and talking," I explained. "Suppose I spent my winters bowling and skiing and dancing and everything. What would I understand about the human soul?"

"True," said Jim, who was putting on his goloshes.

"Bowling," I went on, wishing to explain this thing fully to Jim, "bowling is the perfect recreation for us moderns. The bowl is large and heavy. It is just about the size of the rock the average person, man or woman, would like to throw at his boss. The bowl is flung along a polished wooden alley down which it can be seen going, with speed and power, towards the wooden pins, standing so proudly and solemnly and stiffly. Those five pins are the perfect representation of everything the average

94

person detests. Stiff, upstanding bosses, or bullying parents, or, as the case may be, stiff-necked aunts or neighbors or fellow workers in office or shop."

"You've got it," said Jim, rising to put on his coat.

"So the bowler," I warmed up, "sees the bowl he has flung racing down the inevitable alley towards those stiff and helpless pins. There is humor and joy in that sight. To see the bowl bearing down, about to hit those stiff, stupid creatures and send them knocking into one another and flying in all directions. The savage joy and satisfaction that fills the spirit of the bowler when he or she sends those pins crashing is nothing more or less than the expression, harmless and economically safe, of the wish-fulfillment of what he would like to do to the people he has to live with."

"You said it," agreed Jim, putting on his hat with a look of great purpose.

"Where are you off to?" I inquired.

"I'm going bowling," said Jim. "I've got to sublimate a lot of wild animal out of me. If I don't go and bowl a few frames, there's no telling what I might do."

"Anything gone wrong?" I asked anxiously. "No financial troubles?"

"No," said Jim, "but there are times when I feel there is no use talking any more. It is time for action."

"It's years," I confessed, "since I was in a bowling alley. I'll come along."

So Jim and I marched through the snowy night to a bowling academy a few blocks from our office, and as we walked, we chatted about sport and what a curious thing it is.

"Sport," I explained, "is just war in miniature. Rugby, hockey, lacrosse, all those games, are just two miniature armies at war. Even golf and tennis are fighting, without breach of the law. Ages ago, men used to smash each other with clubs; now they hit a ball, but the violence is there and the struggle, the contest, and the conquering of the other fellow."

"We're savages," put in Jim, "all right."

"As a matter of fact, Jimmie," I said, "it is just silly to indulge in all this talk about abolishing war while at the same time we encourage sport. The spirit in them both is identical. If we are really serious about ending war, we should first end sport. Let us abolish sport, as being wicked, primitive, vicious and likely to keep alive the baser instincts of humanity; and then we can take on the abolition of war with some hope of success."

"Fishing included?" Jim inquired, walking faster.

"Ah, no," I said. "Fishing and hunting are truly civilized sports. They have to do with the perfectly natural pursuit of one's food. It is competitive sports that should be abolished."

Always Competition

"Civilization, Jim," I said, "is cockeyed. It wants everybody to be tame and to give up war; yet it lauds sport to the heavens. It makes as its highest ideal the unselfish citizen who lives to serve his fellow man; and at the same time it perfects an educational system for equipping everybody to compete with, and beat the stuffing out of, everybody else."

"There will always be competition," said Jim. "Even if we ever do reach that heavenly state you speak of, with no more war, no more sport, no more competition in business or industry, with 1,997 million people in the world working an hour a day and at leisure the rest of the time, there will still be guys trying to talk everybody else down."

"No, Jim," I triumphed, "because by then there will be nothing to talk about. We will be at perfect peace."

So we arrived at the bowling academy and climbed the stairs to the upper floor where a distant thunder told us the bowling was going fast and furious. It was a lively scene. The rolling thunder of the bowls, the merry chatter of the crowds gathered all at one end of the big chamber, gave an extraordinary impression of vivacity.

There were groups of business girls, a few small squads of older women; and men of all ages, from high school kids up. Even in the eyes of the middle-aged women, there was a certain warlike expression, a flush on their faces, that bore out adequately my theory that bowling is a sport of sublimation. What these ladies were doing to their husbands, by remote control, when they hurled those wooden balls down the alley, only an amateur psychologist could guess. How many school children were not getting their heads knocked together as the result of these five pins going flying, only a poet could surmise. The younger women and girls were attending to their smashing and havocking with a quiet gusto. I observed one slim, mousey little girl who looked as if she were president of a girls' Bible class, and the way she took a furious run and sent that ball skirling and skating down the polished alley to smack the pins leaping into the air gave some idea of how pious she would be by Sunday. She was eliminating all the spleen out of her system on Wednesdays.

Jim and I took a bench down the side and watched the fun.

"I don't see any of my acquaintances," said Jim.

"Maybe when the crowd thins," I suggested, more to be friendly than from any desire to hurl balls, "the two of us might . . ."

"Swell," said Jim.

Some bowled slow and took all the pins; others bowled slow and took none. Some bowled with athletic fury and sent the pins leaping. Others bowled equally furiously, and their bowls entered the gutter along the side and came to naught. But even just watching was fun, because there was the eternal mutter and rumble of the bowls followed by the loud and martial crash and clatter of pins. It had a busy, noisy, smashing air about it all. A satisfying sound of damage in this prim and rubber-tired and skilful trafficked world. All the motor car collisions you always expect but never hear, all the things going wrong that you expect but never see in this busy machine world, were being balanced up here in this bowling alley, where even slim, lithe young girls, like Tarzan's sisters, heaved bolies and bunged things to pieces, deliberately.

"Jim," I said, "there might be something in this bowling."

So when the crowd, along about ten o'clock, began to thin, and when presently an alley became vacant, Jim and I walked up and engaged it and removed our coats and hats, and pulled up our socks and cuffs, and prepared for a little sublimation.

"I'm giving names," I said, "to each of those five pins. The one in front is . . ."

And I told Jim the names of five people of our acquaintance whom I would take pleasure in belaying.

"You go first," I said, "and show me how."

Away down at the far end of our alley, a young man with red hair was reclining gracefully, and his job was to reset up the pins and send the bowls rolling busily back to us along a special trough.

Jim picked up a bowl, and after calculating carefully, bent down and sent it hurtling along the shining hardwood. It clipped the No. 4 pin, Mr. So and So.

"Good," said I, with pleasant thoughts of that gentleman lying in a gutter.

With his second bowl, Jim laid down three pins with a whirling and defeated scatteration. His third bowl neatly took the last and final pin.

"Good," said I. "Now set the same five gents up for me."

I reached for a bowl, but unfortunately, at the very instant I took hold, the first of Jim's three bowls came rolling smartly back home in the trough and smacked my fingers cruelly. Now it is not that I am a particular baby, but you understand a man who lives by a typewriter and whose only true sport is fly fishing, sets great store by his fingers. Therefore if I behaved a little excitedly and danced about and yelled and shook my fist at the young red-headed fellow down at the far end, I am not ashamed.

But it seemed to me I could see Mr. So and So, the No. 4 pin, grinning with a leer from ear to ear as I carefully picked a bowl up in my injured hand and prepared to sock him. Thus I let go with great if not very controlled power, and the bowl bounced on the hardwood, skidded a few yards and then leaped on to the next alley, just as a member of a neighboring alley let his go.

The man in charge came over and said:

"Easy there, sonny. And don't bounce em, see?"

My second bowl, rendered more delicately, rolled three-quarters of the way down and then weakly sidled off into the gutter. By now I could see all five of my enemies sneering openly at me, especially the No. 5 pin, which distressed me, as I only put him in at the last minute and up until now had no real grudge against him. He was just to fill out the five.

The Hang of the Game

So I let bowl No. 3 go with some snort in it; some nyah; some nghhh!

But in making the back swing too forcibly, the bowl slipped from my numbing fingers and flew backwards; I heard a wild bellow; a crash; cries and shouts; and then Jimmie and the man in charge both had me by an arm each. The teams of young men from the alleys on either side crowded around with indignation and fury on their faces. They were all shouting scornfully and arguing at the same time. But the theme of their complaints seemed to be "Throw him out!"

"You can't take it, eh?" I taunted. "You even want your sublimation to be namby pamby, huh? Can't take it, huh?"

Of course, good old Jimmie was squaring off, and picking up our hats and coats all this time, and slowly edging me towards the door.

"Anybody wish to put a little action in it?" I shouted above their rude remarks, and I could see a man leaning against the wall, rubbing his stomach anxiously. And my last glimpse of the alley showed my five enemies, away down at the far end, all standing stiff and rigid, but seemingly convulsed.

Jim snapped me out the door and we ran down the stairs with vulgar sounds pursuing us.

"Heaven help me," said Jim, as he assisted me into my overcoat out on the street, "if I ever take you anywhere with me again."

"Don't you give a man a little time to get the hang of the game?" I demanded.

"You don't have to act like a maniac."

"I was doing a little sublimating," I explained humbly, "and I got kind of carried away, I guess."

"You," said Jimmie, "and your sublimating!"

Suddenly the rabbit made a right-angle turn . . . the cop turned into the ditch right on its tail.

100

To
The Swift

April 10, 1937

"Look at that bird," cried Jimmie Frise, "look at it travel!"

"It's a flicker," I said, looking out the car window. We were zooming along the highway. "Sometimes called high-hole or yellowhammer."

"But look at it go," shouted Jim, who was stepping on the gas. "We're hitting forty."

"It's a member of the woodpecker family," I explained.

"Never mind what family it belongs to," said Jim, "just

look at the speed it's got."

"Its favorite food," I declared, "is ants. And for the purpose of obtaining ants from their holes in the earth, you will note the flicker has a very long, round, slender, sticky tongue."

"For Pete's sake," shouted Jim, "lay off and look at that bird dangle, will you? We're hitting forty-five and we haven't gained a yard on it."

The flicker, with a final leap in its curious rising and falling flight, came to rest against the bark of a tall dead tree. Jim slackened the car speed to normal.

"Boy," said Jim, "I had no idea birds could go so fast."

"That isn't fast," I stated. "Forty miles an hour is one of the slow-going speeds amongst birds. The humming-bird is believed to travel at the rate of 110 miles an hour."

"Get away," said Jim.

"It's a fact," I assured him. "As the crow flies, it is about 2,000 miles to Mexico, where the humming-bird goes for the winter. So a humming-bird can go to Mexico in a couple of afternoons, stopping to see the sights on the way, in the Yellowstone Park and the Grand Canyon and so forth."

"How about ducks?" asked Jim.

"Canvasbacks have been paced by aeroplanes," I stated, "at a speed of 90 miles an hour."

"Then," said Jim, "I've been leading them too little. I've been shooting ten feet behind them."

"If you are going to turn all my information on natural history into facts for your gun," I said, "I will hardly be inclined to inform you. However, it would take a better mathematician than you to figure out the speed of a duck, plus or minus the velocity of the wind, head or tail, taking into account the exact distance in yards the ducks are from you, so as to have the flight of your load of shot intersect exactly the flight of the duck at the precise one-thousandth of a second that intersection must occur . . ."

"How fast," asked Jimmie, "do black ducks fly?"

"They're slower," I said. "They go about fifty to fifty-five. So do partridge. A pheasant goes about forty to forty-five."

"Their normal gait," reflected Jim. "A mile a minute,

normal speed. And we men move, normally, at about two and a half miles an hour."

"Yes," I said, "birds do get about."

"What's the fastest land animal?" asked Jim.

"The Indian cheetah, a kind of leopard," I said. "It can catch any deer or antelope in the world in less than one hundred yards, and it doesn't quite hit fifty miles an hour. But it's only a sprinter, like all the rest of the animals. An antelope can go around forty miles an hour, but it tires. All animals tire. Their hearts and lungs aren't meant for sustained effort. But birds can go for hours. Some of the plover leave Baffin Land and go straight to Little America in the Antarctic, all in one jump."

Science Means Knowing

"For Pete's sake," said Jim, who was driving along watching for more birds to race.

"Yes," I said, settling down to the discussion, "and some of the Arctic terns . . ."

"Who," said Jim, "collects all that stuff about Arctic birds, and why?"

"How do you mean, why?" I demanded indignantly.

"What I can't figure out," said Jim, "is where all this stuff about birds and animals and insects and things comes from. Who gets it? What for? There are so many other things to do in the world, like shoe-making and raising wheat and working for banks and so on. Yet apparently there are guys up in Baffin Land watching plover go away. And guys down in the Antarctic waiting and watching for the plover to arrive. Why? Who? Which? And who pays for it?"

"Jimmie," I said pityingly, "science is above all mercenary motives. You wouldn't understand. Science means knowing."

"Knowing what," said Jim, "and why?"

"Science wants to know everything," I explained. "Nothing is too small or irrelevant or indifferent for science to know. Science observes and records everything. Science has an army, a vast, international army, devoted, self-sacrificing, more patriotic to science than any men ever were to any mere country, giving their lives to the gathering of knowledge, each in his different sphere. Watching birds, trees, animals, seeds, wind, rain, rocks, soil, sun, stars, butterflies, bugs; in fact, there is nothing you can think of, try as you will, that is not the subject of intense study and observation by some scientist or group of scientists."

"What's the object?" asked Jim.

"To know all," I quoted, "is to understand all. When these vast armies of science have probed all life to its uttermost and secret end, life itself will be understood. Truth will reign at last."

"Yes," said Jim, "but what have the habits of Arctic terns got to do with truth?"

"Well," I said, "for example, one scientist spends his life up in Baffin Land living in an igloo and eating blubber, in order to discover that terns can keep on the wing for 100 hours. Then another scientist makes a study of the tern's heart structure, to see how it differs from human hearts, say."

"Ah," cried Jim, "some day they're going to graft bird hearts into us humans, so we can live for a thousand years!"

"No, no," I shouted, "science is not interested in mankind at all. It is only interested in truth."

"For what?" shouted Jim.

"Don't let us quarrel," I said. "If you don't understand about science, you don't understand, that's all. Some people live their lives perfectly happy, never wondering. Others are filled with a divine and insatiable curiosity. You are interested in a flicker, because you see it travelling parallel with you at a speed that surprises you. The minute you have observed that phenomenon, which is purely personal, you forget all about flickers. But I, on the other hand, like to know all about flickers, what they eat, how they are specially equipped for that eating, how they live, where they nest and why, how many eggs they lay . . ."

"It's just a hobby of yours," said Jim. "Now my hobby is Russian pool. I like to know how a ball, hit a certain way, causes another ball to do a certain thing. You want to know why about birds, and the answer doesn't matter.

I want to know how about pool balls, and the answer saves me maybe fifty cents a game. Knowing about birds isn't going to get you anything. Knowing about pool balls makes me money. See?"

"Between us," I muttered, "we're a pretty good example of the human race."

"Mmmmm?" said Jimmie.

"Look," I exclaimed. "Ahead of us there, see that bird?"

Jim crouched and stamped on the gas. The car leaped forward.

"It's a dove," I said, "a mourning dove, one of the fastest fliers, doing maybe fifty miles an hour. If it just follows the road . . ."

"Watch me," said Jim.

Just Observing Nature

He kept his foot on the gas, and the car gained speed furiously. The dove, with quick, headlong wingbeats, fled away ahead of us. Jim got the needle up to fifty-five miles and still the dove, as if co-operating, held its course straight up the highway.

"We're gaining," cried Jim.

"Don't overtake it," I warned, "and scare it. Maybe we can pace it for an even mile, and then we can write to the ornithological journals. This is what I mean. We're scientists, Jim. We are adding to the great . . ."

A brown blur zipped alongside of us and passed us.

"Speed cop," gritted Jim, taking his foot off the gas and touching his brake carefully.

The cop coasted ahead, watching us in his mirror and slowing as we slowed. We drew off to the side and stopped. The cop, the very set of his head indicating outraged sensibilities, swung his large leg stiffly off his cycle, and lifting his goggles off stern eyes, turned and walked back towards us.

"Weh-hell," he said. "Weh-hell, what a hurry we are in this morning."

"Sir," said Jimmie, "we were doing a little scientific experimenting."

"Experimenting, eh?" said the cop. "Weh-hell."

He put a very unfriendly little chuckle in between that weh-hell.

"Yes," I inserted, "we're interested in ornithology. We were pacing a dove."

"Pacing a which?" asked the constable, flipping the leaves of his notebook for a nice clean page.

"We're interested in birds," I explained. "The speed of birds is a subject of intense interest to the scientific world. We were in the act of pacing the speed of a dove, a mourning dove, when you overtook us."

"Professors, eh?" said the cop.

"No," said Jim, "not exactly professors. But the world of science includes many like us, who contribute millions of important facts to science. For example, how fast does a dove fly? Professors could come out in their cars every day of their lives, looking for a dove to race, to test its flying speed, and never see a dove, much less encounter a dove actually flying straight along a level stretch of highway. Such coincidences come only once in a million years, and we were actually checking the speed of that dove when you interrupted us."

"How fast was it going?" asked the constable.

"We had it held at exactly fifty-six miles an hour," I stated.

"I paced you at sixty-one," said the cop.

"We were trying," I said, "to establish a fixed distance from the bird, and hold it for one statute mile, and then you had to come along and spoil what would perhaps have gone down in history as one of the greatest records in science."

"That certainly is too bad," said the constable, closing his book and returning it to his breast pocket. He rested his elbow on Jim's window. "Why don't you have some kind of sign painted on the back of your car? So we'd know you were making experiments like that?"

"That's what I was saying," I explained. "These opportunities to serve science only come by accident, and you never know when the chance will offer. It may be a hundred years now before somebody, somewhere, has another chance like this to pace a dove. Maybe a whole century."

"I certainly am sorry," said the cop, sadly. "I'd hate to be the guy that spoiled a thing like that, specially as I am very interested in nature myself."

"Are you?" I said eagerly. "What's your specialty?"

"Oh, I don't know," said the cop, modestly, "I observe groundhogs and things. I take a special interest in hawks. I've followed a hawk around eleven concession roads."

"Really?" I cried.

"Oh, yes," said the constable. "Life is pretty dull, just sitting along the road, looking at cars whizzing by and chasing silly people and having to listen to all their excuses. Nature is a great relaxer, don't you think? I get a lot of pleasure out of just observing nature, kind of."

"Well," I said, "it's funny how we meet, we nature lovers."

"Say," said the cop, suddenly, "there's a jack rabbit up here a-ways; he gives me a race every now and then. A great big jack rabbit. I never thought to see how fast he goes. There's an idea."

"It certainly is," Jim and I both agreed.

A Right-Angle Turn

"I'll drive up ahead, you follow," said the cop, "and if he's around we can chase him and see his speed. My goodness, I'm sorry I never made a note of his speed. I bet he goes forty."

"Oh, no," I laughed, "not a jack rabbit, not forty. I bet a jack rabbit can't do thirty."

"Thirty!" said the cop indignantly. "Listen, boy, this is one of the biggest jack rabbits in the country, I tell you, and if he doesn't go better than forty, I'll eat your shirt."

"Let's go," said Jim, who liked the cop best as a nature lover and didn't want to get his rougher nature roused.

"Let me drive," said I.

The cop tramped his engine into life and with a wave led us on. For six miles we scooted, being scientists, at about fifty. Then the cop slowed and coasted cautiously ahead of us.

Suddenly, out of the ditch by the road, a large fuzzy

fawn-colored jack rabbit leaped, with a big lazy leap, and a flirt of his hind legs.

Straight down the side of the highway he ran, in long, bounding leaps, his ears laid back or cocked forward, as he seemed to look back, out of his bulging eyes, over his shoulder.

The cop increased his speed. So did we. The rabbit let her out. The cop crouched low and drew closer to the rabbit. We drew closer to the cop.

I watched the needle. It rose from twenty to twenty-five; to thirty. It hung at thirty, while the cop with all the cunning of a scientific observer, increased his pace almost imperceptibly. And the jack rabbit, with ears laid flat, began to let fly with his long hind legs to show what a jack rabbit, in this spring of the year and the young wheat sprouting, can really do.

"Thirty-two," I cried tensely. "Thirty-five. Jimmie! Thirty-seven! This will make a wonderful record to send to the scientific journals!"

I was clutching the wheel, keeping as close as I dared to the motorcycle, and the cop, all crouched down, was keeping as near as he dared to the brown racing ball of fawn.

Suddenly the rabbit made a right-angle turn, a wild leap across the ditch.

The cop turned right on its tail and automatically I whipped the wheel to the right, and, with a thud and a rattle and violent bump, we too went into the ditch, narrowly missing the cop, who, with his cycle, was all of a heap up against the snake fence.

"Hurt?" I shouted, scrambling out of the car.

"Forty-one miles an hour," said the cop.

"Thirty-seven," I corrected. "Thirty-seven. I was looking at the speedometer."

"Look here," said the cop, rising angrily, "I've a good mind to run you in so as to have your speedometer tested. I tell you it was forty-one. I was looking right at the speedometer when the darn thing made that jack-knife turn . . ."

"How about getting me out of the ditch?" demanded Jim, who was still sitting in the car and looking a little shaken.

"Okay," I said.

With a fence rail, the cop and I turned Jim's wheel and eased him up enough to let him drive safely out of the ditch. There was only a slight shimmy in his front axle. The cop tried his machine out and it was in good shape. He walked over to us.

"Well," he said, grimly. "What do you say? Was it forty-one or not?"

"It was forty-one," said Jim emphatically. "I made it forty-one."

"How about you?" said the cop.

"I guess it was forty-one, all right," I said.

"Okay," said the cop, buttoning his breast pocket where the little book is kept.

Something

They were running
around in circles,
trampling all over the
newly planted
seedlings. . . .

Has To Be
Done

"I see by the papers," said Jimmie Frise, "that there are 15,000,000 dogs in North America.

"The country," I admitted, "is really going to the dogs."

"The less able the world is to keep dogs," said Jim, "the more the fashion grows. In more spacious days, when there were no motor cars and every home had some ground around it, I could understand everybody keeping a dog. But under modern conditions it seems to me keeping a dog should be a privilege accorded only those who are qualified. And the qualifications should be enough ground around the home for the dog to play in without risking his life and limb on the trafficky streets. And the other and more important qualification should be that the dog owner would have enough intelligence to control and master his dog."

"Well, we'd qualify," I agreed. "I must say your old Rusty has almost a human intelligence. And as for my Dolly, she is practically a member of the family."

"We've taken the trouble," explained Jim, "to train and educate our dogs. Rusty and Dolly are, you might say, modernized dogs. But some of these wild animals that gang up and rove this neighborhood are not only a nuisance but a menace. Here I am putting in my garden for the next couple of nights. Now, Rusty is trained. He knows what a garden is. He never runs on the borders or tramples the young plants. You never catch Rusty digging up the garden or messing about the bushes."

"Dolly's the same," I said. "In fact, I have seen her

chasing other dogs out of our garden. Many's the time last summer I have watched Dolly walking about the garden looking at the flowers just as if she were a human being and enjoying them exactly as a human being."

"Yesterday," said Jim, "I happened to look out the back window and what did I see? Three of those mutts of the neighborhood, two half-breed collies and a wire-haired terrier, actually burying bones in my perennial borders."

"I'd say," I said, "that most of the people in our neighborhood keep dogs by force of habit. They apparently take no pleasure out of them, as we do in Rusty and Dolly. They let them out in the morning, probably giving them a kick as they go, and they let them in at night. And for the rest of the day, those dogs just run at large.

"It looks like it," agreed Jim. "Something will have to be done."

"Now there's that apartment house along the street," I reminded him. "I was counting the dogs in it. There are eight families in that house, and I'll be jiggered if there aren't nine dogs. One family has two of those bug-eyes Pekes."

"That apartment house," stated Jim, "has no yard at all. It has a concrete area at the back entirely filled with garages. It has no front lawn to speak of. Where do those nine dogs run?"

"On other people's property," I declared.

"Exactly," said Jim.

"We certainly ought to do something about it," I asserted. "And we, as dog owners and dog lovers can't be accused of being prejudiced against dogs either. I am one of the first to get my dander up when any of these anti-dog people begin their annual uproar about dogs running at large in the city. It is usually about now, when people are putting in their gardens, that the rumpus begins. But there is reason and moderation in all things, including dogs."

"All I expect of other people," agreed Jim, "is that they control their dogs the same way I do."

"That's it," I supported. "Let that be our slogan. And if we dog owners start the agitation, it will go a long way further than if these anti-dog people try to do anything."

"I can't understand a man or a woman not loving a dog," said Jim. "If I were going to start a political party or a new religion or something, I would take a census of the homes of the city, and where there was a dog, that home I'd invite in."

"I doubt if there ever was a villain who owned a dog," I agreed.

"No food and no love is wasted in a house where there is a dog," declared Jim. "It gets what is left over of both. You can tell all about a home by the dog."

And with this kindly thought we went to our appointed tasks for the afternoon.

After supper, seeing Jim in his garden south of mine, and I not being quite ready to plant my annuals, as I like the garden to be best in September rather than July when all my family are away, I strolled down to watch him, Dolly joining me.

Jim had the little boxes of petunias and zinnias all laid out ready to be planted; the crimson nicotine and verbenas, the sweet william and orange flare cosmos. I helped him carry the little boxes of plantlings and distribute them around the borders where they would variously go. Old Rusty and Dolly solemnly accompanied us as we moved here and there.

"Look at them," said Jim, fondly. "See how intelligently they watch us. They know what we are doing. They are interested. I bet they even realize that presently, as the result of this work of ours, the garden will glow and smother with flowers and sweet scents."

With tongues out, the two sat, a little stoutly, maybe, a little over-fed, most amiably following us.

"No silly romping," I pointed out. "No nonsense. There's dogs, Jim."

And we proceeded to set the plants, Jim scooping the holes with his trowel and I breaking out the seedlings with blocks of earth from the basket complete. We petted them down. Nasturtiums, marigolds, mourning bride, lantana. Clarkia in clumps because it is stringy, verbenas well separated because with their multi-colored stars they will reach and spread. The best part of May is the

113

end where we plant the annuals.

To sort out some weeds that Jim bought to eke out the foot of his garden, such as sunflowers and some coarse climbing nasturtiums for along the fence, we went indoors and down to Jim's cellar billiard room, and we had hardly been there a minute before Jim glancing out the cellar window let forth a wild bellow.

Rusty and Dolly had wandered off when we had come indoors, and as we reached the back door, there were no fewer than seven dogs holding a kind of canine gymkhana in the garden.

"Hyaaah," roared Jimmie, hurling a flower pot at them.

There was a red setter, a police dog, a scrub collie, a wire-haired terrier, a goggle-eyed Boston bull, a Scotty, and a big overgrown Springer spaniel, weighing about sixty pounds, a kind of a mattress of a dog, brown and white.

They were racing in circles trampling all over the newly planted seedlings, ducking around perennials just decently leafing out of the earth, plunging through spiraea. . . .

"Hyaaaaaah," we roared, charging into the yard.

All but the Springer spaniel, without so much as letting on they saw us, raced out of the back gate and down the street, like a gang of panting, laughing hoodlums.

The Springer, with a look of interest, was braced in behind Jim's loveliest Japonica bush, watching us with rigid tail and cocked head.

"You!" said Jim, advancing cautiously.

"Easy, Jim," I warned. "Get behind him and chase him out."

"I'll catch him," said Jim, "and deliver him to his owner."

"He may be cross," I warned.

But the Springer spaniel, all feathers and wool and burly good nature, was far from cross. He was for play.

With a slithering, dirt-flinging spring, he wheeled and raced along the wire fence, every bound crashing him heavily on to some little cluster of freshly set and fragile plantlings.

"Hyaaahh," we roared at him.

With a skid and a slither, he would halt and watch us,

tail wagging frantically and mouth agape in a wide grin of joy.

"Don't try to catch him," I said, "he thinks we're playing."

"I'll show him if we're playing," gritted Jim.

He advanced, half crouched.

The Springer, with an ecstatic slither, was off again, crashing through a bed of Darwin tulips with his whole sixty pounds and plunging into a young spiraea bush as if to play hide and seek.

"Aw," moaned Jim terribly.

"Shoo him out, shoo him out," I yelled. "He'll romp in here all night, if you let him."

"Rusty, Rusty," roared Jimmie into the evening.

"Hyuh, Dolly, hyuh, hyuh," I cried, "sick 'im.

But Rusty and Dolly were absent at the one time we needed them.

"Here, help corner him," commanded Jim. "You come along that way and I'll come this way and we'll corner him by the house."

So we slowly converged.

The Springer waited, with sly, joyous eyes, until we were almost on him before, with a plunge that flattened the spiraea and carried him horribly on top of the whole cluster of long slender orange flare cosmos plantlings, he burst the blockage and tore across to the opposite border of the garden and took refuge, playfully, behind a perennial phlox that, in another month, is the wonder of the whole district, so gorgeous a magenta is it, with its hundred blooms.

"Oooooh," moaned Jim, "if he crushes that!"

"Throw something at him," I insisted. "Make him get out."

"Now I'm determined," declared Jim gratingly, "to catch him and deliver him."

"Very well, then," I decreed. "Shut the gate."

So while Jim shut the gate, I picked up a few odds and ends, the trowel, a couple of flower pots and a garden stake. And with these as ammunition, I drove the astonished Springer into the corner by the house while Jim charged in and grabbed him.

115

He struggled furiously and then angrily, growling and snarling.

"Get the rug out of the car," panted Jimmie, wrapping himself around the astonished and frightened dog.

I nipped over and snatched the car rug and brought it. Jim managed to roll the big spaniel in it, leaving only his head out.

We straightened ourselves up and dusted off.

"There," gasped Jim. "Now, Mister Springer, I know where you live."

"What will you say?" I asked. "Better get it planned so you won't just arrive in a temper and say worse than nothing."

"I'll simply say, 'Sir'," said Jim, "here is your dog. It came into my garden and trampled all over my newly planted seedlings. It plunged through my tulips and bushes and crushed my perennial phlox. I do not blame the dog. I blame the owner of the dog who has not taught it to behave and to respect gardens'."

"Then what?" I asked.

"I'll hand him his dog," said Jim "and warn him that if the dog damages my garden again, I will take steps that will astonish him."

"Let's go," I said, because the big Springer was patiently struggling within the folds of the car rug and I was afraid he might work free.

Jim carried the extraordinary bundle down the street. The owner lived about eight doors south.

"Ring the front door," said Jim. "We'll make no back door peddling of this."

I rang. I rang twice. I rapped.

"They're out, I guess," I guessed.

"Maybe they're in the yard," said Jim, starting around.

In the yard, on the clothes line, some sort of chintz curtain was hanging. My Dolly, sweetest and gentlest of dogs, was clinging to one corner of the curtain; taking little runs and a swing, and chewing and growling secretly and furiously with the fun.

Fair in the middle of the yard, in a bed of resplendent parrot tulips, elderly and amiable Rusty, most intelligent of all the dogs I ever knew, had all but vanished down an enormous hole he had dug, just his hind quarters and tail showing until Jim's shout brought him backing out to look, with easy innocence, over his shoulder.

"Jim," I said low, "drop that dog and let's sneak."

The kitchen window of the house next door squealed suddenly open and a red-faced lady put her head out.

"What are you doing with that dog in the blanket?" she demanded chokingly. "I'll tell Mr. Hooper on you. The very idea. And look what those brutes are doing to his garden and to Mrs. Hooper's chintz."

Jim unrolled the Springer and he landed heavily and ran straight for Rusty, his hackles up.

"Those two creatures," shouted the lady above the racket that Rusty and Dolly were making in a fight with the Springer, "are the worst nuisances in the entire neighborhood. And yet I catch you in the act of trying to smother the loveliest, kindest dog in the whole city."

Jim and I withdrew up the side drive and then turned and called Rusty and Dolly. They came, being glad to leave the Springer who was beginning to get rough.

We hastened up the street, the Springer pursuing us with hoarse and angry barks.

"It's always the other fellow's dog," reflected Jim.

"And to somebody, I suppose," I said, "we are always the other fellow. Shoud I let those people know who chewed the chintz?"

"No," said Jim, as we turned into Jim's yard. "The Springer will get the blame and it will all even up in the long run. He deserves the blame to make up for what damage he has done elsewhere."

"These two," I said, "never get any blame around here."

"Oh, well," said Jim, starting to walk along the borders to re-set up all the little seedlings, "they behave around home. What more can you ask?"

So Rusty and Dolly, their tongues hanging out, followed us along, sitting down behind us to watch the job and getting up to follow whenever we moved five feet, and we rubbed their towsled heads and scratched their eternally itchy chins, and they looked up at us with half-closed eyes of adoration and perfect understanding.

July 31, 1937

Cool
At Last

"We descended the ladder into a humid world and carried the ice down to the skiff."

"Ice," said Jimmie Frise, "is badly needed at my cottage."

"And mine, too," I confessed. "Welcome the day when they get electric power through this neck of the woods and we can have an electric refrigerator."

119

"Nonsense," cried Jim. "Going for the ice is one of the few remaining pleasures of the summer cottage. Look at us. Radio. Indoor plumbing. A gasoline pump for the water tank."

"On a day like this," I sighed, "I could wish to be modern in all things."

"The swellest kind of a day," retorted Jim, "to go for the ice. Think of the dear old ice house. How cool it will be inside. The dark damp sawdust. It will be a pleasure just to get inside it."

"Will you row the boat?" I asked.

"I'll row over," said Jim. "You row back, after you are refreshed by a few minutes in the ice house. It will revive you the way no swim can. Not even a cold shower."

"You know," I mused, "on a day like this, Jim, we Canadians can pat ourselves on the back, just for being Canadians. Just for surviving. Did it ever occur to you that perhaps no place on earth do they have such extremes of temperature as we have in Canada? In the summer, it is as hot as India. In the winter, it is colder than Russia. To be a Canadian, you've got to be made of real stuff."

"Asbestos," agreed Jim, "on the outside, with wood alcohol for blood."

"In about four hundred years," I stated, "I wouldn't be surprised to see the Canadians take on a racial type, a sort of cross between the Negro and the Eskimo. We will gradually acquire a dark brown hide as the result of our summer. And a smooth featureless skin covering a thick layer of blubber, like the Eskimo, as the result of our winter. I bet we'll be an interesting looking people, in about four hundred years."

"Come and get the ice," said Jim, rising.

"Sit down, sit down," I begged. "This is a day for thinking twice about everything. Let's think about things for a while. The sun will be going down in a couple of hours. We can get the ice any time."

"Our ice box," said Jim, "has got a humid smell. It is moaning for ice."

"You skinny fellows," I sighed, "are lucky. There you are dressed in thick canvas, and as cool and dry as a cucumber. Here I am in shorts and a cotton scanty, and I'm oozing slowly to pieces. Suppose you get the ice today, and I get the ice to-morrow? For both of us?"

"No," said Jim. "It takes two to get the ice. One to dig in the sawdust, and the other to crowbar the hunk out and chop it. And then it takes two to carry the ice down to the boat."

"You could drag it," I explained.

"If I have to go alone," said Jim, "I'll bring only my own cake of ice. Depend on that. I look upon going for the ice as one of the last old-fashioned pleasures of summer resorting. Summer cottages are getting so sissy the last few years that there is really no sense in having them. You might as well be at home. In former days, you went to a summer cottage not so much to escape the heat—for really you don't escape the heat—as to restore your mind and spirit by a taste of the simple life. Your cottage was primitive. It had outdoor plumbing. You carried the water up in pails and washed in a blue enamel basin hung on a nail at the back door. You had a wood stove and the kitchen was so hot, your wife never had to worry about reducing. The summer cottage kitchen reduced her. There was a woodpile for you to work in on cool evenings or gray mornings. There was no radio. You had candles and sometimes lamps. The mattresses were made of hay and you could hear the mice tickling along the rafters and gnawing, the minute the last lamp was blown out at night."

"I remember," I sighed, happy just to be listening.

"Alas," said Jim, "we have conquered even the mice. Even the ants. We've got modern spring beds, running water, electric light in most of them now . . . it's not for the simple life we come to summer cottages now."

"What is it we come for?" I dozed.

"Fashion," said Jim. "Custom. That's all it is. As a matter of fact, most summer homes nowadays are more refined and civilized than city homes. They are civilized, sophisticated. We used to get bitten by mosquitoes. Now it is the love bug that bites them at summer cottages."

"Mmmmm," I muttered reminiscently.

"Here, wake up," cried Jim. "Let's go."

121

"Jim," I said earnestly. "I love to hear you talking about things like that. You're quite a moralist, do you know that?"

"I'm the ice man," said Jim, champing the jaws of his ice tongs. "Come on, snap out of it."

Which I did, and sufferingly went and got my ice tongs and followed Jim down to the rowboat. It is a pleasant row over the little bay to J. Brown's Ice House and Lumber Yard. Even on such a day as this, with a copper sun glaring and hurling down its thunderous heat, it is pleasant to sit in the stern of a rowboat and watch an aggressive man like Jimmie pulling at the oars. I think the nicest sensation in the world, on a day like this, is not to feel your own muscles working. It is positively pleasant to behold another man's arms bending and hauling, and feel your own arms resting limply along the sides of the boat. Actually pleasurable to see somebody else bending and straining and feel your own back loose and limp against the cushion behind you. They talk about the lovely sensations of athletic sport, the consciousness of action. The sensation of inaction is far lovelier.

And presently the skiff grated on J. Brown's beach, scarred by generations of ice haulers such as we, and we unbarked. The J. Brown Ice House and Lumber Yard has, over a period of fifty years, come to a splendid working arrangement with the cottagers of our neighborhood. J. Brown himself long ago discovered there were far too many things expected of him around a summer resort to allow him to dance attendance on an ice house. So you just go and help yourself and at the end of the season you go and settle with J. Brown, making a rough estimate of the number of hunks you have taken. It is the same with lumber. If you need a few scantlings or a plank or two, you help yourself. J. Brown comes around in the evenings and closes the ice house door in case it is left open, and asks any small boys who might be around if they have seen anybody take any lumber. It's the best way to do business, as a matter of fact. Worry and keeping accounts is what takes the pleasure out of business.

Jim led the way up the ladder of the ice house and

cheered me up the climb with shouts of delight.

"Just wait till you get up here," he cried. "It's like a cave. It's air conditioned."

So I hurried up the ladder, and it certainly was a lovely sensation to step out of the slanting rays of that angry declining sun onto the soft damp sawdust into the shadowy cool of that old cracky ice house.

"You dig, Jim," I said. "I'll chop."

So Jim took the old spade and stabbed around in the sawdust to find the latest layer of ice. He found it and proceeded with large graceful sweeps to fling the sawdust aside. He presently bared a dark and wetly gleaming cake of ice. With the crowbar, he wedged it loose from its neighboring cakes and then stood back.

I rose and took the axe. There is something about chopping a cake of ice that wakes the sculptor in a man. The feel of the little flying chips of ice is pleasant to the skin. To make a nice neat split in the big cake of ice is the aim of every good family ice man. To achieve this, you tap and tap, cutting a channel along the top, then a channel along both sides, and finally, you give it a good sharp crack with the axe, and it splits with the grain, neat and tidy.

"I-Told-You-So" Stuff

Jim, while I was chopping slowly and carefully, was prodding around in the sawdust with the spade to see what the neighbors had hidden as usual. Sometimes it is a parcel of fish, wrapped in newspaper and secreted deep in the sawdust against the ice in a corner. It is interesting to examine these packages and know just what is going on in the community. It helps you separate the liars from the fish hogs.

Jim found two packages and we ceased work long enough to open and examine them, however one was a leg of lamb and the other was two cartons of eggs.

Then, having successfully parted the huge block of ice into two handsome sections, one for each of us, we hooked the tongs into one of them and hauled it to the door and dropped it down.

"One piece at a time," decreed Jim. "It will give us all the longer in this cool place."

We descended the ladder into a humid, heavy world, and carried the ice down to the skiff after dousing it with the pail of water. Then we returned to the ice house for the second load. Inside, it was so lovely we both sat down in unspoken agreement and lit cigarettes. Jim saw a swallow's nest stuck against the side of the wall and we proceeded to study it.

And suddenly the ice house went dark.

"The wind," said Jim.

"There's no wind," I stated. And plowed across the sawdust to push the door open. It was stuck. I kicked it. It would not open.

"Jim," I said, "the door's fastened."

"Don't get excited," said Jim, "it's too hot."

He looked through a crack in the ice house wall.

"H'm," said Jim, "it's old J. Brown himself. Hey, Mr. Brown."

But Mr. Brown has been hard of hearing for twenty years. I found a crack to peep through and saw J. Brown slowly walking along the beach path that leads past the lumber yard to J. Brown's house, half a mile away, which is also the post-office and the general store and the dance hall and garage and everything.

"Hey," I roared through the crack. "Hey."

But J. Brown was aimlessly walking away, scratching his head and stopping to study his lumber piles and to gaze out across the oily lake under the descending sun.

"Hey," we harmonized. And pounded on the walls.

"Jim," I said, "there will be nobody else for ice at this time of day."

"If you had come promptly, when I wanted you to," said Jim.

"Never mind that I-told-you-so stuff," I snarled. "Figure how we are going to get out of this."

"He padlocks it," said Jim.

"And leaves the key in the padlock," I sneered. "So near and yet so far."

"Have you got a pocket knife?" asked Jim, feeling his own pockets blankly.

"Mine's in my tackle box," I accused.

"Well," said Jim cheerfully, "we're cool at last. Let's enjoy ourselves."

It was already dim in the ice house. The light that came through the cracks was red and warm. But it was not cheering.

"Let's try for a loose board," I commanded.

But Jimmie just started to scout around for a soft spot, scooped himself a nice nest and lay down with a comfortable sigh. I was left alone to go around the walls, trying each board for a loose spot, panting and prying and shoving; in vain.

"Don't grunt so," said Jim, luxuriously.

"Jim," I stated, "I have nothing on but these shorts and this cotton dicky. I'm liable to catch pneumonia in here."

"Oh, I don't think so," sighed Jimmie, snuggling.

"I've been sunburned," I informed him loudly, "and my skin is tingling now and I've got little chills already."

"Keep moving then," said Jim, dreamily. "Shovel or take reducing exercises or something."

Nothing Like Exercise

Instead I tried looking out the cracks for the sight of rescuers. I went all around the ice house once more, feeling for loose boards. I tried a couple of long shouts out a knot-hole, but Jimmie protested violently.

"What's the good of all the racket," he demanded. "We've just got to wait until our absence is noted and they came hunting for us."

"They'll never notice our absence," I declared. "We're never home on time. They won't even think of us until midnight."

"We're cool, aren't we?" said Jim. "We're comfortable? This sawdust is soft, isn't it? All right, sit down, relax, and let's continue that discussion you were so anxious to continue a while ago. Let's see, it was about Canadians being made of the real stuff. Asbestos hides and anti-freeze for blood, wasn't it?"

"Jim," I said carefully, "I'm starting to shiver. I'm getting a chill. I'm going to catch pneumonia."

"What do you want me to do about it?" demanded Jim. "Slap you to restore circulation?"

"I'm sunburned," I said. "We can't do that."

"Then," said Jim, "exercise. Swing your arms. Bend. Walk briskly about."

I kept still for a minute to make sure I was really starting to feel shivers, and then, feeling shivers, I began to exercise. Jim just lounged in the sawdust, his hands behind his head, watching me. I swung my arms, bent my knees, ducked, swung, in the exercises familiar to all old soldiers and all fat ladies. I worked myself into a nice warm flush and then discovered that, if I stopped, the cold clammy air of the ice house really did chill me.

"Now you've done it," I informed Jim. "Now I can't stop this monkey business."

"Walk around," said Jim.

But, as it was now dark in the ice house, walking about knee deep in loose sawdust was not amusing at all. So I continued, slowly, the calisthenics.

"I can hear you puffing," said Jim, from his comfortable resting place. "I wish I could see you."

I made no answer. Every man, in his life time, makes some such a friend as Jimmie.

"I was thinking, this afternoon," continued Jim, "on the veranda there, that you were looking kind of flabby. This will do you no end of good."

Still I made no answer.

"At our age," went on Jim, "men have to guard against a creeping desire to just loaf and sag and go limp."

"Jim," I said firmly, "please shut up."

"I'm a moralist," said Jim. "When I am not an ice man, I'm a moralist."

And then we heard a boat engine. It sounded like Jim's. It had the same miss, the same sputter and stagger and almost stop.

"That's your engine, Jim," I shouted, leaping for a crack to yell out of.

"If it is," said Jim, still unmoved, "whoever is running it certainly won't be able to hear you yelling."

So there we had to wait, helplessly listening to the engine, sometimes thinking it was coming our way and sometimes thinking it was going away, until at last there could be no doubt that it was coming straight for the ice house beach. Then we heard laughter and answers to our calls. The kids unlocked the door, J. Brown always leaving the key in it, and they asked us what we were doing.

"We were going to spend the night here," said Jim. "It's the coolest place in the country."

But they persuaded us to come on home.

Goosie, Goosie, Gander

August 7, 1937

*"Hey," came a shrill voice . . . down the
lane and out the gate came a fierce
little woman. . . .*

"What gets me," said Jimmie Frise, "is the way everybody is so sure they are right nowadays."

"We're perfectly sure, for instance," said Jim, "that
our form of government is the only possible thing for
self-respecting people. Germany is perfectly sure her
system is the only possible. Italy the same. Russia, the
same, breaking her neck not only to believe it herself but
to teach the whole world to see the light."

"We've done a little neck-breaking, in the past," I
pointed out.

"It wasn't so bad," said Jim, "when we were the only
nation showing others the glory of our particular kind
of freedom. But nowadays, with every nation that isn't
defunct trying to stuff itself down the throat of all other
nations, it's getting a little tedious."

"Tedious is the word," I agreed.

We were driving in the country and it is always best to agree with the man at the wheel. If you argue with him, he takes his eye off the road to turn and look at you.

"I blame education," said Jim.

"The more you educate the people," I said, "the more enlightened they become."

"That was the theory," declared Jimmie, "but it hasn't panned out. It ought to be pretty evident now that you can't change people's ideas. They are born with their ideas, the same as they are born with their noses or the color of their hair."

"Oh, come, come," I said.

"All right," cried Jim, "how do you explain the universal disagreement? For the past hundred years there has been an enormous and universal growth of education and enlightenment. Think of the vast expansion of publishing, until books and papers, billions in number, are likely to bury mankind. Think of the movies and the radio in recent years, flooding the humblest places with facts and truth. Yet, instead of becoming gradually of one mind, we have never been of so many drastically different minds in human history. Not only do nations disagree, but our provinces disagree, and we ourselves all disagree, until you can't find two men in the whole world who think alike."

"Ah," I said, "education has set us free to think as we like."

"No," said Jim. "All education has done has been to give us self-confidence in our ignorance."

"A fine opinion you have of yourself," I suggested.

Nobody Changes His Mind

"Common sense and a casual glance at human history," said Jim, "will show you that wise men are few and far between. Would there be one really wise man in every hundred men?"

"I hardly think so," I admitted.

"Then," said Jim, "ninety-nine of a hundred of us are ignorant."

"Speak for yourself," I stated.

"Yet," said Jim, "education has taught us to read, write and talk. It has given us self-confidence. It has removed all doubt from our minds. However, as our beliefs and ideas are born in us, and can't be changed any more than the shape of our noses, why, all we can do is give vent to these inherited notions."

"I think for myself," I declared.

"You think," said Jim, "the way you were born to think. In former days, unless you had some special energy that made you stand out as a leader or thinker or firebrand, you kept silent. Your ignorance did not matter.

But now, you need no special energy. You are forced to go to school, by law, until you are a competent blatherskite. If you are a little backward in expressing yourself, they put you in special classes, where your self-confidence is nourished by extra tuition. This has been going on now for about fifty years. The result is the universal cockeyed disagreement between nations, communities and finally individuals."

"What do you suggest?" I inquired. "That we put an end to education?"

"I think everybody ought to be taught," said Jim, "that they can't help thinking what they think. It ought to be dinned into them, in the first book and the fourth book and in high school and at the university that the unfortunate notions they entertain cannot be altered by any process whatsoever, with this result, that we would all understand one another, at last."

"It would fill us with contempt for one another," I cried.

"And who else?" laughed Jim.

"Why, it's an awful thought," I protested.

"Think, now," said Jim, "of all the people you have known, across the years, your family and friends, whom you have known since childhood, can you think of a single one, a single, solitary one of them who has ever really changed his mind?"

And across the years, I couldn't. I marched them past my mind, one after another, my brothers—little fat boys and bold young soldiers and middle-aged business men; my friends—beloved chums, gay companions of my youth, comrades of my manhood, comfortable friends of my present life; and of them all, not one but was in the beginning what he is in the end; the same slants on life, the same ideas, notions, beliefs, subdued a little, maybe, or modified out of politeness or wisdom; but abandoned, never. Changed, never, thank God.

"Jim," I said, "education is a good thing, even so. It points out to us a lot of things we wouldn't perhaps have noticed in life, as we passed by."

"Agreed," said Jim, "but education is too proud. It ought to be humbler. It ought to wear the uniform of the

spieler on a sight-seeing bus. For that, in the end, is all
it is."

"A Nice Thing You've Done!"

We were driving through a very pleasant country full
of ripening fields and bulging cattle and orchards already
twinkling their fruit at us, and there was the first faint
hint that in a few weeks the deep winds will be blowing
all this away, all this green beauty that we think of as
the permanence, and autumn, winter and spring only the
impermanence.

Being in so pleasant a land to look upon, we were
dawdling, so when a car with a voice like a ripsaw came
from behind and, in a great swirl of gravel and dust,
threw us to one side as it plunged past, our country
humor was disturbed.

"The dang fool," said Jim, recovering his control of the
car, "where is he going at such a rate and what does it
matter?"

Through the swirl of dust, we saw the stranger's car
lurch violently, swing to one side and then continue, with
increased fury, on its way.

And then, just as we came to the place he had lurched,
we saw a flock of geese scattering wildly up the ditches,
and, on the side of the road a great fawn-colored gander,
huge wings outspread, feebly flapping its last.

"Pull up, Jim," I shouted. "A hit and run driver."

Jim drew the car to a stop and we leaped out and ran
back. The geese were making a great hissing and trum-
peting, as they stood looking back at the great dead
master. For now he flapped no more.

"What a magnificent bird," I said, gazing down on him.
"And Thanksgiving only a couple more fattening months
away."

"It must have been concussion," said Jim, squatting
down and touching the bird. "No signs of being smashed."

"Hey," came a shrill voice, and from a little farmhouse
on the side, down the lane and out the gate came a fierce
little woman.

"Let's carry it in to her," said Jim.

So we picked the goose up by a leg each and started
toward the house, like mourners.

But the little woman came, all hunched up with purpose, straight at us.

"Well," she bit off, "a nice thing you've done."

"Madam, we did . . ."

"That's the prize gander," stormed the little woman with a thin, penetrating voice, "at five fall fairs last year."

"A car came past . . ." I began.

"And," shouted the little woman huskily but raspingly, "it was going to bigger fairs this fall. That there gander . . ."

"We didn't do it," shouted Jim, unexpectedly.

"No, no. I suppose the gander hurled himself at your car," screeched the little woman with a surprising reserve supply of voice. "I suppose you were travelling by at fifteen miles an hour when suddenly the gander just took a dislike to you and dashed his brain out against your car. I tell you, that gander was worth eight dollars if it was worth a cent. I been selling eggs sired by that gander for fifty cents apiece. Breeders from all over Ontario . . ."

"Madam," I roared, still holding one of the feet of the poor gander, "I tell you we had nothing to do with it. We saw another . . ."

"Oho," cackled the little woman with a break in her voice like those old stars of opera on the radio, "so I suppose it was some other car hit him and you just stopped to help the poor beast."

"That's it," shouted Jim and I together.

"A likely story," said the little woman witheringly. "A couple of gentlemen from the city passing along a country road see a gander brutally run over by another motorist and they stop to lend a friendly hand. Heh, heh, heh."

"That's precisely the case," we both stated firmly.

The little woman was convulsed with mirth.

"You stand there," she squealed, "trying to tell me that. We'll see what the magistrate thinks."

"Madam," I announced loudly, "we are two humane men. When we saw the poor creature fluttering on the roadside, in the wake of a scoundrel who plunged by at fifty miles an hour . . ."

"I saw you," hissed the little woman, crouching accusingly, "pick the bird up and start toward your car with it."

"Madam," we shouted, dropping the bird as if on a word of command.

When Education Doesn't Help

"Oh, I've got your car number," grated the little woman, "and you'll get a summons. And there's been too much poultry killing in this county to suit the neighborhood. You'll catch it."

"We can prove we didn't kill it," I insisted.

"But you can't prove," cried the little woman triumphantly, "that when I came running out my door, you had stopped your car and picked the goose up."

We stood gazing at one another heatedly. The poor beast lay at our feet in the dust.

"How much did you say the bird was worth?" demanded Jim.

"Eight dollars," said the little woman firmly, "and I wouldn't take a dollar less than four for him."

Jim and I dug. Two dollars each.

"We keep the goose," said Jim.

"If you want a run-over goose, you're welcome," said the little woman grimly.

She held the money in her hands, counting it two or three times. Jim and I picked the goose up by the feet and carried it, with dignity, to our car and laid it on the floor of the back.

"What's the use," demanded Jim, as he got behind the wheel, "of being humane? Why try to be decent? You're always misunderstood."

"Education wouldn't help that situation we've just been through," I sighed, as we got under way and bowled less observant through the country scene.

We heard a hard, thudding sound back of us. It was the gander.

"Jim," I said sharply, "he's come to."

"Good," said Jim, "we'll sell him to some farmer down the road."

Enormous flapping and scrambling sounds came from

the back, then a fierce hiss, and my hat was kicked
smartly over my eyes.

"Hey," I ducked, "pull up the car."

On the shoulder of the road, Jim and I leaped out,
while the gander, fierce head erect, neck feathers swell-
ing, hissed malevolently and flapped his immense wings
helplessly around in the back of the open car.

"Open the door, let him out," I ordered.

Jim opened the door and with a wild honk the gander
leaped to the ditch and waddled furiously away toward
the farm we could still see in the distance.

"Follow him," I commanded. "Turn the car around and
follow him."

"To heck with him," said Jim.

"He's heading straight home," I cried. "Let's get our
money back."

"To heck with him," said Jim, but he got in and turned
the car around and slowly and at a snail's pace we followed
the silly bird back a mile. It waddled in the ditch and it
took the fences; it paused and it sat down and rested; it
turned its wicked eye on us if we got too close and simply
stood its ground. It threw clods of sod at it to hurry it,
and instead, it came back and attacked me, so losing
twenty feet of good ground.

Finally, the weary and obese bird turned in its home
lane, where with royal honks all its family welcomed it.
We walked up to the farmhouse and rapped.

No answer. We went back to the barn and hallooed
and howled and howled, but no sign of living person was
to be seen. Across the fields, nobody moved.

"We'll wait," said I.

"So will she," said Jim.

"I wouldn't wonder," I accused, "if that gander was
trained to play dead when cars go by. I wouldn't wonder
if she's trained that bird to pretend to be hit . . ."

"What good does education do anybody?" said Jim,
sadly.

"Well, I've got my own ideas," I said.

"So has everybody," sighed Jim, getting in the car and
starting it. So I got in too and we went on our way.

Confidence
Men

August 14, 1937

"I whisked gently the brown murmurous ball."

"What's that humming?" demanded Jimmie Frise.

"An aeroplane, isn't it?" I suggested. We were sitting on the cottage veranda, thinking.

Jim lowered the front legs of his chair to the floor and leaned out to look.

"It's not," said Jim, alarmed. "It's right here on the veranda."

He jumped up and posed in listening attitudes here and there, cautioning me to hist and keep quiet, although I was still doing nothing but think.

"It's bees," cried Jim.

And then he saw them, a swarm, clustered at the top of one of the hollow veranda posts at the far end.

"Look!" he shouted, backing away, "look at the mess of bees. Thousands of them all in a solid swarming ball."

I got up and joined him. It was a striking spectacle. Like a queer blurred football, the swarm of bees hung in a round, solid mass, crawling, tremulous, filling the air with a high vibrant though faint roar as of a million wings.

"Jim," I informed him, "you are beholding one of the most fascinating spectacles in nature. A lesson to all mothers and mothers-in-law is being enacted before your eyes."

"Are they likely to stay here?" demanded Jim, retreating farther, as stray and apparently excited bees zoomed a little crazily around.

"Is there a hole anywhere up there?"

"Yes," said Jim, "there is a little knot-hole right up near the top of that pillar."

"Then," said I, "you have bees."

"I don't want bees," cried Jim. "Let's drive them away. I'll get a smudge."

"Too late, Jim," I assured him. "By now the queen bee has gone in the knot-hole and down inside that hollow post. There, safe and sound in her carefully chosen domain, she is resting after her marriage flight. In a little while, when this queer marriage dance of her followers is ended, they will get furiously busy, bringing pollen and honey and building wax cells. In a few hours, there will be honey galore in that veranda post."

"Not if I can arrange it otherwise," said Jim. "There are enough things around a summer cottage without making welcome a million bees."

"The loveliest companions imaginable," I declared. "One of man's oldest companions, save the dog. Until comparatively recent times there was no such a thing as sugar in the world. Man depended on these little creatures to provide him with all the sweet he knew of. These marvellous insects, for countless ages, were man's only flavoring, his only candy, his sole dessert."

"To heck with them," said Jim. "Let's get them out of this."

"Jim," I pleaded, "sit back a minute here and watch.

You may never see the like of this again. Do you know what is happening? One of the strangest mysteries in all nature, and a lesson to all mankind."

"I'd rather they wouldn't have time to get settled," said Jim.

Their Mystery Dance

"In some beehive in this neighborhood," I explained, "this queen been that has now come to your house had built herself a beautiful dominion. She had reared an immense number of progeny, neither male nor female, but neuter. They were workers. There she dwelt while her slave-children went forth from sunrise to sunset every day, amidst all the perils of life, to gather pollen and honey and to produce from their own insides bees-wax to build countless cells."

"I don't like their hum," said Jim. "It's getting angrier."

"They're still half dopey," I explained. "During the swarming they seem to go half asleep, as if under a drug. Now, when she had a vast hive built by her slave-children, the queen proceeded to lay a few extra select eggs. These were queen eggs. The eggs hatched, the grubs of the queens began to grow, in their cells, being royally fed on pollen and honey by their faithful and sexless brother-sisters."

"Brother-sisters?" demanded Jim.

"Well, since they are neither, they might as well be either," I explained. "Royally fed, these baby queens were, and in due time, after they have grown to full grubhood, they go into a queer state of rest, called the pupa."

"I was never much interested in bug science," said Jim, looking anxiously at the great living ball of bees. "I like engines and things like that."

"Aaaah," I fixed him with my finger and eye, "but Jim, when these queen grubs go into their curious beauty sleep from which they will wake as lovely big queens, sort of Mae Wests of beedom, a funny thing happens in that hive. Yes, sir. The minute the grubs go to sleep, and all is quiet and no more feeding of them to be done, suddenly the whole hive seems to go on tip-toe. From all corners of their world, from the clover fields and the gardens, the sexless worker bees return all to the hive. And then, as in a conspiracy, they begin to go into their mystery dance. They seem to grow numb. They act queer and stupid. They begin to crawl all over one another, as if drunk. And then the old queen, the maker of all this tiny empire, appears to give a command. She crawls to the door, her swarm of workers following her drunkenly, and away she flies, to seek a new home, with all her revellers coming staggering through the air after her, and here, my dear Jim, she is!"

"You mean," cried Jim in astonishment, "that she just went and left her rightful home to her daughters?"

"Precisely," I stated. "While she is here hiding in that veranda post, with all these pie-eyed courtiers and servants of hers trying to waken from their stupor, back in the old home, a queer silence reigns. In a little while those sleeping beauties of queen grubs will begin to stir. Maybe it is the strange silence that disturbs them. They will begin, in their little silken bags, to squirm and stir. And then a more curious thing than ever happens."

"What?" said Jim, eyes still on the brown resounding ball in the veranda corner.

"The first sleeping beauty to waken," I stated, "chews her way out of her silken cell, a beautiful queen bee. Without delay, she walks to the opening of the hive and flies forth into the sun and sky. From somewhere prince bees who have been hatched out amongst the workers and have spent their lives in sheer idleness, bumming about the gardens, come in answer to some secret call that new queen utters, some soundless high marriage call, and one of the princes marries the new queen and she returns to her hive."

"And how about her queenly sisters?" asked Jim.

"That's the miracle," I said. "They're queens, just the same as the first one to chew her way out. But because they were not the first out, they are doomed to be spinsters. And their job, poor things, is to act as royal handmaidens to her majesty the new queen, while she lays hundreds of eggs that will hatch out into sexless slave children and so the whole rigamarole goes on again."

"I'll be jiggered," said Jim.

"Yes, sir, they act as handmaidens, feeding the grubs of the workers as they hatch and generally being skivvies to that royal sister who was first out."

"Don't any of them ever sneak off and get married on the sly?" asked Jim. "Secret marriage sort of thing."

"No," I replied. "If you want a thrill, you ought to read 'The Life of the Bee,' by the Belgian poet, Maurice Maeterlinck. But doesn't all this I tell you make a big difference in your attitude towards that swarm of bees?"

"No," said Jim, "a bee is a bee. And no amount of beautiful talk is going to change that."

"Jim," I said, "don't you realize what a wonderful lesson those bees are to humanity? They've been socialized millions of years before we humans were. They've worked out a successful pattern of life."

"I suppose you suggest," said Jim, "that we should all raise families of workers, the first six born, let us say, will just be toilers."

"Correct," I agreed.

"Then," said Jim, "the last or seventh born shall be a sort of royal pet, and be waited on and tended by his or her slave-sisters and brothers, and be permitted to marry and carry on the race."

"Correct," I admitted.

"What a swell life for the first few born," scorned Jim.

"Ah," I countered, "but what a swell life for the last born. Never to have to work. Just to live and be beautiful and happy and raise up six children to support the royal seventh. Aaaaah!"

"I don't like bees," declared Jim firmly. "I never did like them. And now I like them less than ever. Why, it's a heck of a system."

"You should sympathize with them," I argued. "Look at all those poor muddled creatures there, the slaves. Born without hope of posterity, working their little lives away for the good of the race."

"To make more slaves," cried Jimmie. "The whole theory of bees is just to make slaves. I think they've got the wickedest system in all nature."

"All nature are slaves," I pointed out.

"Not a bull," shouted Jim. "A bull is no slave, loafing around a pasture, eating and sleeping. That's the life. We should go to the bull not the bee for our object lessons from nature."

"You'll get to like these bees," I said tenderly. "You just read that book by Maeterlinck."

"I'm going to get a smudge," said Jim, with determination.

"Naw, naw," I laughed. "My dear Jim, a smudge won't do any good. All you need is confidence."

"Confidence?" said Jim, eyeing me.

"Confidence is all," I assured him. "I've read up all about bees. Nobody need fear them. They are highly civilized. If you have confidence they will never sting you, no matter how you handle them. A true lover of bees can walk right in and handle them, open their hive, move them about, take their honey, and if he has confidence, the bees will absolutely not molest him. His confidence communicates itself to the bees."

When It Comes to Demonstrating

"Lets see you," said Jim.

"See me what?" I exclaimed.

"Let's see you use your confidence on them," said Jim. "Get them out of this."

"Ah," I explained, "I am a thinker. I leave action to those who are directly interested. I am inspiring you to be confident, to walk up and whisk those bees into a box and carry them off to some farmer in the neighborhood. He'll welcome them."

"Whisk them?" said Jim.

"Yes, that's what the true beeman does, he just whisks them quietly into a box and takes them back home."

"I'll get you a whisk and a box," said Jim, starting away.

"No, no, Jim," I protested. "You ought to realize that among civilized people, those who do the studying and the thinking are not expected to do the doing."

"So?" said Jim, sarcastically. "You're one of those guys we support in luxury to do all the heavy thinking? But when it comes to demonstrating to some poor guy the way to do it . . ."

"Confidence, Jimmie," I remonstrated. "Surely you have confidence?"

"Show me," said Jim, so coldly that I just sat there while he went and got a whisk and box.

"Have you got any netting?" I asked, when he returned with the articles. "Any mosquito net or wire net?"

"Confidence," said Jim, "is all."

"Jim," I said, "I have absolute confidence that those bees are dopey and full of wedding spirit of some kind, but any pictures I've seen of bee handlers, they had a sort of screen over their heads."

"Was that," demanded Jim in a hushed voice, "all bunk you were telling me about Maeterlinck and the wedding flight and all?"

"Jim," I said, "where would we be in this world if we didn't believe the philosophers?"

I took the whisk. I took the box. I walked confidently and coolly up to the end of the veranda. I stepped up on a ladder and with a slow rhythmic motion of my arm lifted the whisk.

I whisked gently the brown murmurous ball.

The neighbors, afterwards, said that the shouts and roars lifted them one foot off their afternoon siesta stretchers. One neighbor said he thought it was the end of the world.

Some of the neighbors prescribed soda, others salve, and one masterful neighbor insisted that good plain mud was the best, in liberal poultices.

Anyway, lying there in a darkened room, I did not care what they poulticed me with so long as it was cool and damp.

And lying there, defenceless and not in the mood to argue, I heard Jimmie explaining, at great length, and not without eloquence, the mystery of the swarming, the mystery of the lone queen born into a strange and silent hive; and he concluded:

"What you need, of course, in dealing with bees, is confidence. I've always had confidence in bees. But I'm confident they'll sting me. See?"

The storekeeper picked up the bill
and examined it closely. "I can't
change this," he said,
suspiciously.

Twenty Dollar Bill

September 25, 1937

"What is it," asked Jimmie Frise, "that makes us Canadians so desperately respectful of authority?"

"I don't imagine," I replied, "that we're any more respectful of authority than other people. The English, for instance, or the Germans."

"Ah," argued Jimmie, "yes, but the Germans have to be respectful or have their fingers jammed in doors in internment camps. And as for the English, it's only put on. Did you ever try to pull a little authority over an Englishman?"

"If I had the authority, I think the English would recognize it as readily as anybody else," I informed him.

"If you were an Englishman and had the authority," corrected Jim. "They have a sort of agreement among themselves, a working agreement. But you take Canada. In one province the church is the authority. In another province, the premier kicks out the banks and all kinds of established organizations and what he says goes. We're all the same. Somebody up top says what's what and we all submit. There are no outbreaks. It isn't as if these authorities had any tough gendarmes or black shirt police to back them up. And it certainly isn't by agreement that these big shots are set up. Not by general agreement anyway. I'm beginning to think Canadians are the most docile people on earth."

"Remember the Chinese," I protested. "Or Eskimos."

"All I'm thinking of," said Jim, "is that cop back there at that fork in the highway. The way he ran up alongside of us and arrogantly turned us into the side of the road with a flick of his head."

"He was perfectly right," I said, "you didn't slow down at that fork. There was a sign distinctly saying 'slow to 15 miles'."

"I've passed that fork a hundred times," said Jim, "and there never was a cop there before."

"That isn't the point," I assured him. "That law is the law whether there are any cops looking or not."

"I don't mind how many laws we've got," said Jim, "so long as I am not humiliated in the enforcement of them."

"You're not mad at the cop," I jeered. "You're only mad at yourself for being so humble."

"I wasn't humble," stated Jim. "I was only sensible."

"You squawk about Canadians being docile," I laughed, "and if ever I saw a docile Canadian, it was you when

that cop nodded you haughtily to the side of the road and
then bawled the daylights out of you."

"I stared him straight in the eye," cried Jim.

"Yes," I said, "with your eyes wide and alarmed and
full of an expression of deepest respect and humility."

"We'll Have to Be Smart"

"Oh, I did not," protested Jim heatedly.

"I did nothing of the kind. And anyway, how could you
see me when you were cringing down in your seat as if
God had suddenly appeared at the car window."

"You were servile," I declared. "You even called him
sir."

"An old habit," said Jim, "I contracted in the war. It
was his khaki uniform."

"Well," I agreed, "it does seem absurd to me the way
we kowtow to a cop. The way they bawl us out, the tone
they take, you would think they were magistrates instead
of cops. I don't think we should put up with it."

"The next cop," said Jim, "I'm going to put in his place,
if he so much as uses a tone I don't like. He's an em-
ployee."

"Now you're talking," I said, sitting up hopefully to
watch for cops."

"There must be some guilty conscience in us, or something," mused Jim. "We Canadians must be descendants
of people who came to this country fleeing from the law.
All servility is based on fear. We must have some inherited fear of cops."

"I wouldn't doubt it," I said guardedly, (because after
all what do we really know about our great-great-grand-
fathers?).

"I wish," sighed Jim, "I had inherited something else
from my ancestors than a guilty conscience. Craftiness,
for example. I had a great-uncle Zebulon who was the
craftiest man in seven townships. If I was crafty, I'd
know what luck we were going to have to-night in finding
the best place to go fishing."

"It won't be hard to find out," I said. "A few discreet
inquiries around the village."

"Listen," said Jim, "there are only nine houses, one

147

general store and a gas pump in this village. Every man in the place is a musky fisherman. Dyed in the wool. The muskies at this time of year have left the weed beds and the deeps and have come in shore, along by the rocks and boulders. They are easier to catch and fight harder than at any other time of year. It is the peak, the glorious climax of the fishing season. These villagers look upon this season of the year as their share of the fishing. All summer long they have been working madly for the benefit of tourists who were getting all the fishing. Now the tourists are gone, and it's the villagers' turn. They will resent us even arriving."

"We'll worm it out of them," I assured him.

"We'll have to be pretty smart," said Jim.

"We can watch where they fish," I reminded him.

"Yes, and waste half the morning trying to locate them," argued Jim. "They'll all be out before daybreak."

"Jim," I said, "you've got a poor opinion of country people. All we need to do is the old trick. Buy a few things at the general store, ask a few questions. Buy some gas, ask a few questions. Rent a boat, ask a few questions. Put two and two together, and there we are."

Full of a Great Quietness

The tiresome flood and tumble of summer traffic had left the highways. The fields were bright and hard, the hills beginning to garb themselves in color. The miles rolled past as we floated deeper into the musky country where civilization and the rocks were coming to grips. The farms grew fewer and more curiously laid out in fields bordered with shoals of primitive rock. We saw the first maples gone gold and red. The villagers are right. This is the best time of year to go fishing.

We passed through Peterboro and the villages began to be farther apart. We left cement for gravel and gravel for sand, and finally entered a lovely narrow road winding amidst rocks and tall hardwood forests which we knew, according to our written directions, was the road that led to our happy destination where, along the rocky shores of a twisted and many-bayed lake, the big muskies, sick of the rotting weed beds, lay in the pure shallow shore water, waiting for something to wiggle past them, such as a well-cast lure.

And towards evening, we came to the village, full of a great quietness amidst all the equipment it had for summer, its park, its brightness, its shuttered outlying cottages. We cruised slowly down its one street, planning our campaign of reconnaissance.

"The general store, first," I suggested.

And in front of the general store we drew up. It was the regular general store, with its ceiling covered with galvanized pails, bundles of hats, baled socks, boots. One side, groceries. Other side, drygoods. Back, hardware.

Three or four men lingered leaning on counters as if expecting nothing to happen anyway.

"Good evening," we said cheerily, in that easy city fashion. Our entry seemed to break a spell that had been holding the general store in thrall.

Everybody muttered except the storekeeper, an elderly gray moustached man who eyed us over his spectacles and said nothing. He went ahead quietly parcelling something out of sight.

Jim and I wandered slowly down the store, looking at the merchandize to see what we could reasonably buy as an excuse for visiting the store. Something inexpensive but useful.

"I think I'll get a pair of overalls," I said quietly, whispering through my nose.

"Nice bandanas," murmured Jim. "How about a couple of bandanas each? Handy fishing."

"You get the bandanas," I muttered, "and I'll take a hank of that clothes line. Good stuff to have in our kit for an anchor."

"O.K.," agreed Jim, "and two or three cans of tomatoes. I don't like drinking this weedy water; and canned tomatoes are swell."

"O.K.," I muttered, as we turned and proceeded to the front of the store where everybody was covertly taking us in out of the corners of their eyes.

The storekeeper finally finished whatever he was doing and came and stood facing us, planting both palms on the counter.

A Faint, Cold Smile

"Good evening," said Jim, amiably. "How much are those bandanas?"

"Two for a quarter," said he, handing down a sheaf of them.

We examined them carefully.

"Two of them," said Jim pleasantly.

"How much is that clothesline?" I inquired with a winning smile.

The storekeeper looked at me expressionlessly and said:

"Twelve cents."

"I'll have one," I informed him enthusiastically.

But it seemed very difficult to rouse any response. Jim strolled back, eyeing the shelves speculatively, and I followed.

"What did I tell you?" Jim murmured. "We're suspected."

"Ask about the fishing anyway," I whispered.

"Not now," said Jim shortly. "Hostile."

Our murmured conversation was not lost upon the silent company in the store. The merchant was tying up our small purchases in paper.

"Three cans of tomatoes," said Jim. "About a pound of cheese and a box of soda biscuits."

The storekeeper slowly gathered these items and set them on the counter. He seemed to be waiting. So did all the others. A curious electrical feeling was in the dim air of this goods-crowded store.

"That will be all," said Jim, reaching into his pocket.

"Here," I said, "you bought the gas. I'll attend to this."

"No," said Jim, "I want this changed."

And he laid a crisp new $20 bill on the counter.

The storekeeper's hands paused in the act of spreading a piece of wrapping paper. He stared at the bill. He picked it up gingerly and examined it closely. He held it up to the light.

"I can't change this," he said.

"Can you get it changed handy?" asked Jim.

The storekeeper looked long and steadily at Jim. Then

he shifted his gaze to me. There seemed to be a faint cold smile in his eyes.

"No," he said.

"Can any of your gentlemen?" said Jim, turning to the others standing back in the store.

They stirred and looked away and shook their heads.

"Here," I said, diving into my pocket. But I had only seventeen cents and a ten-dollar bill, the expenses of the fishing trip, plus any sudden emergencies.

"Can you change the ten?" I said, tossing down the nice new Bank of Canada dix.

The storekeeper reached but cautiously and picked it up and examined it closely. He shot a quick look around at the men standing behind us.

"No," he said. "Sorry."

"Well, heh, heh," I said. "I've only got seventeen cents. How much have you got, Jim?"

"Just a dime," said Jim.

"You can take two cans of tomatoes," said the storekeeper, "or the two bandanas. Or the rope and one can of tomatoes. Or . . ."

"Maybe the gas-pump man can change it," suggested Jimmie.

"Do You Mean to Insinuate?"

All eyes turned to one of the men standing back of us. He, it seems, was the service-station man.

"Sorry," he said. "All I got is tens myself."

In every face, all of a sudden, suspicion. Cold, undisguised suspicion.

"Gentlemen," I said, "do you mean this money is no good?"

I picked up my ten and examined it closely.

"It may be all right," said the garage man, he was a heavy set and sulky type, "but there has been some phoney money spread around this country lately."

"Do you mean to insinuate," I demanded of the public at large, "that we are trying to pass bogus money? Are you accusing us of being criminals?"

Nobody replied, but the storekeeper turned his back

151

and began replacing on the shelves the articles we had almost bought.

Jim and I looked anxiously around at the faces. They were mostly averted, and there was no friendliness on any of them.

"Could you tell us," asked Jim, "if there is a boarding house in the village open or anywhere we can put up for a couple of nights?"

Everybody looked at us.

"We're here for a couple of days' fishing," I put in.

"Fishing?" said the sulky garage man. "Well, my mother takes in a couple now and then."

"Mrs. Tom is still open, I believe," said the storekeeper.

His and everybody else's face had come to life.

"I'll slip over and see what mother says," said the garage man, buttoning his windbreaker in a business-like way.

"Muskies you're after, eh?" said the storekeeper, breaking into a friendly grin.

"Yes," we said, "but er . . . ah . . ."

"Oh, that's all right," said the storekeeper. "If you want that stuff I can change your twenty easy enough."

"How's this?" demanded Jim, "A minute ago . . ."

"Sure, sure," soothed the storekeeper. But you acted so suspicious when you came in."

"Suspicious?" I asked.

"Guilty as anything, the both of you," laughed the storekeeper, starting to hand down the tomatoes and bandanas again. "Didn't they, gents?"

Everybody smiled and nodded.

"I couldn't figure out," said the storekeeper, whose name proved to be McAndrews, and can he ever catch muskies?—"until you laid down that new twenty, and naturally I thought there was something funny about it."

"Well," said Jim, "if we looked guilty it was only because our real purpose coming in here was to get some tips on where to go fishing to-morrow, but we were going to buy some odds and ends and ask you casually . . ."

"Ah," said Mr. McAndrews, "a guilty conscience always shows."

"All right," said Jim, "here's a straightforward question."

And we got a straightforward answer, and five muskies and we know the first names of the whole fourteen men in the village and we hope to leave a lot of tens and twenties there from now on.

Christopher launched himself into space. The ladder wafted back, under the powerful heave of those wings.

Thanks
A Lot

October 9,, 1937

"What size of a turkey," asked Jimmie Frise, "have you in mind?"

"A turkey," I enumerated, "about the size of a ten-year-old school-boy. A turkey, say, roughly, about the size of a large travelling bag when picked, plucked, singed and trussed up ready for the oven."

"About a 12 or 14-pounder?" inquired Jim.

"Never mind the weight," I assured him. "It's the size I am interested in. You know that sort of box or lid that goes over a sewing machine? Well, I want a turkey, nude, about that size. In short, I want a turkey that won't fit any roasting pan we've got. I want one that can't possibly be got into our oven."

"What's the idea?" demanded Jim. "Don't you want to eat this turkey?"

"Of course," I laughed. "But you see what I mean. Whenever I say I want a real big turkey at home, they always say a big one won't go in the oven. Or that we haven't a pan big enough. Or it will be too big to eat or too tough or too dry or something. I'm going to bring them home a turkey that is a turkey. They will have to go and buy a big enough roasting pan. And they'll have to tie the blame thing's legs down and grease it all over in order to slide it into the oven. They'll have to pack that turkey into the oven the way they get a chesterfield up the stairs on moving day, by figuring and calculating and trying it this way and that way. But I am determined this year, of all years, to have a turkey for Thanksgiving that truly represents the grateful heart."

"It won't be a young bird," cautioned Jimmie.

"Who wants a young bird?" I demanded. "This business of buying everything young, like baby beef and young chickens—why, there isn't any taste to that stuff. The world is getting soft, and no wonder. Eating nothing but veal and baby beef and six-weeks-old chickens. Give me prime beef, one slice of which is as big as a face towel. Give me a good big rooster, with a flavor that is a flavor. I like bacon off a hog that spent some time and thought upon his bacon, every slice as long as your arm."

"An old turkey," warned Jimmie, "is often as dry as a roll of asphalt roofing."

"Not if he is properly cooked," I replied, "with plenty of fat bacon skewered on his breast-bone, and well stuffed with the right kind of dressing. Mix some fresh butter in the dressing, and some nuts."

"Nuts?" cried Jim.

"Whole English chestnuts," I said stoutly, "and whole walnuts and filberts. You've got a good big cavern to stuff when you've got a real big turkey. It's a hole almost a square foot in size. A small boy could crawl right into

it. You need about a bushel of stuffing for the kind of
turkey I have in mind. Loaves of bread, box after box
of biscuits, handfuls of chestnuts, walnuts and filberts,
a slashing big fistful of sage and summer savory, some
onion and anything else you fancy, not forgetting a big
gob of butter to lubricate the beast from within."

"You seem to like turkey," said Jim, as we drove along
the autumn road, turkey bent.

What Might Have Happened

"Carving chickens," I said, "is just a kind of manicure
business, a kind of fiddle-diddle breaking and tearing
apart of a poor little fragile, helpless song-bird. But carving a turkey is a major construction job. You have moun-
tains to break down. You have mighty joints to separate
with knife, fork, sharpening steel and elbows and anything else your family will let you raise above the table
level. And finally a mighty excavation job, with a great
big spoon, digging out the stuffing."

"I like slicing the white meat," said Jim.

"Aaaah," I agreed.

"The way it slices," quivered Jim. "In great big white
tender slabs, with juice running and the smell rising."

"Mmmmmmm," I confessed, staring eagerly over the
farm fields as we passed in watch for the great bronze
figure of a turkey the size of a young horse.

"Still," said Jim, "I don't think we should get all worked
up over the thought of eating that turkey. Thanksgiving
shouldn't be merely an excuse for a colossal bust of eating."

"You're right, Jim," I said, "it's a sacrifice. We should
make it a sacrificial feast. But to get people into a truly
grateful state of mind, you have to fill them pretty full."

"It has been a year to be thankful for," said Jim, looking
at the fat Ontario barns.

"Except in the drought areas," I suggested.

"The true spirit of Thanksgiving," said Jim, "isn't so
much for the things we have got as for the things we
didn't get. For instance, we didn't get any gumboils this
past year."

"And we didn't get hit by lightning," I submitted fer-
vently.

"My car hasn't been wrecked," said Jim, "nor me squashed beneath it."

"And nobody," I contributed, "has persuaded me to mortgage my few belongings and borrow money from my friends and relatives to put into a sure thing in the stock market, only to lose it all."

"I didn't get the itch," said Jim, "though it was very prevalent among my friends."

"And I haven't had a single corn all year," I prayerfully added.

"Lots of people," went on Jim, "have had the appendicitis and all sorts of trouble, but not me."

"I haven't had any toothache," I thought up.

"Nor hangnails," listed Jim, "nor ingrown toenails, nor thumbs hit with hammers."

"Think of the aeroplanes," I said, "that have flown over us, and not one has ever fallen on us."

"Or even dropped a wrench on us," said Jim. "We haven't been shipwrecked. We haven't been run over in traffic. No slivers under our fingernails."

"No plaster has fallen on us from our ceilings," I remembered.

"When you think," said Jim, "of all the things that might have happened to us, we certainly ought to be thankful."

The Spirit of Thanksgiving

"It certainly is far larger grounds for gratitude," I admitted, "than the few good things we did get, like our salary every week or good crops."

"We should give thanks," decreed Jim, "for the things we didn't get. That ought to be the spirit of thanksgiving."

At that moment, in a stubble field this side of a pleasant white farm-house backed with red barns and sheds, we beheld the unmistakable form of an enormous turkey.

He was swelled all up in his pride. He was absolutely square. His head was drawn back and his tail spread wide and his wings were dragging. In a slow, measured pace, like a politician pausing between sentences, he strutted a few aimless steps.

Jim had taken his foot off the gas and we coasted to a stop. He turned off the ignition just in time. Across the bright stubble came the baritone bellow of the bird, a sound like a baseball bat being rattled in a huge syrup kettle.

"Jim," I breathed, "that's him."

"I'll toss you for him," said Jim, anxiously.

"He's mine," I declared grimly.

Jim started the engine again and in low gear we crawled up the lane to the farm house, feasting our eyes on the splendid creature as we passed. He grew more beautiful and desirable with every moment. He was far bigger than he had seemed from the road. He was as broad as he was deep. His plumage gleamed like metal and his enormous wattles, when he slowly turned to face us as we passed, were not merely red. They were magenta. And they hung from his head in great knobby festoons like the ornaments of some pagan Aztec high priest.

As we passed, he began to shiver and shake in a sort of frenzy, stretching every fibre of his being, and suddenly thrust forth his great neck to let go a sound like nothing on earth.

"Hoggle, woggle, goggle!" he yelled.

"Hah, hah, hah," I yelled in retort out the window.

"I bet he weighs 30 pounds," gasped Jim.

"Each side of his wishbone," I gloated, "the white meat will be as big as a rugby ball."

Think of his drum-sticks," cried Jim.

"You could use his wishbone," I said, "for croquet."

We pulled up in the farmyard and a lady in an apron came out, drying her hands.

"We're looking for a turkey," said Jim jovially.

"A big turkey," I added, significantly.

"Ah," said the lady, "I was afraid Christopher Columbus would holler once too often."

"Christopher Columbus?" I asked.

"That's his name," said the lady. "The one out there in the stubble. He's pedigreed. That's his official name."

"Is he for sale?" asked Jim.

"Everything is for sale," said the lady, "considering."

"How much is he?" I inquired.

159

"Wait till I call pa," said the lady, retiring to the house and coming out with a big galvanized horn on which she blew a deep fat blast. This was a well-organized farm.

He's More of a Pet

While the lady went and got a pitcher of cider, Jim and I got out of the car and looked the situation over. It was a beautiful farm. The house was neat as a pin, and brightly painted. The yard looked as if it had been swept. The buildings were all tidy and trim. No chickens or calves roamed loose.

"Look at that barn," said Jim. "Bulging."

"Look at that implement shed," I countered. "Everything as trim and tidy as a would-be foreman's bench."

"Farmers must be in the money again," said Jim, and from the far side of the house came the triumphant challenging yell of Christopher Columbus.

Over the fields came the farmer in long business-like strides. Out from the house came the lady with the cider pitcher. The bright sun glowed.

"Pa," said the lady, as the farmer strode up, "here's a couple of gentlemen to see about buying Christopher Columbus."

"Old Chris, eh," said the farmer, accepting a glass of cider from his wife and hoisting it in salutation.

"We're tired," I explained, "of looking at those poor pallid turkeys they have hanging in the stores. The kind you have to look at their feet to see if they are chickens or turkeys."

"Them," explained the farmer, "are what they call standard market size. The way people are nowadays, they don't want a real big turkey. A nice medium bird is what the market calls for."

"Well, this expedition," I stated, "is a protest against nice medium birds. It isn't any nice medium Thanksgiving we are thinking of staging this year. It's a real old-fashioned Thanksgiving. And no standard market bird will do."

"Christopher is a big bird all right," said the farmer.

"We never did put a price on him," said the lady, pouring Jim a fresh glass.

"We never raise turkeys," said the farmer, "they are too tricky. I stick to the things I'm sure of."

"We bought Christopher," said the lady, "at a fall fair four years ago, just for fun. He was only a little bird then, compared."

"He's more of a pet," explained the farmer.

And from the far side of the house came the echoing roar of Christopher Columbus.

"Now last year," said the lady, "we would have sold him without a thought. But this year, everything has been so good, we never had a crop in all our lives like this year. Everything has turned out, the grain, the roots, the cattle. Why, we even had two sets of twin Jerseys."

"Well," I interrupted, "it wasn't so much for all the good things we have received during the past year that we were planning to stage a special Thanksgiving. It was more in recognition of the things we didn't get, like appendicitis or motor accidents or getting accidentally shot while out hunting."

"That's an idea," said the lady.

"Yes." said Jim. "Just think. All the things that could have happened. Lightning and lung trouble, broken legs and so forth."

"Mercy," said the lady, "now you come to think of it, there is hardly a farm around here they haven't had some misfortune this past year."

The farmer cast an anxious look at his bulging barn and looked nervously up at the sky.

"Still," he said, "in this business, you raise things to sell. And Christopher is in his fifth year. You never can tell what might happen to him some day."

We started to stroll around the house towards the stubble field. Jim and the lady followed, talking earnestly about heart trouble and headaches, fallen arches and whooping cough.

We stood at the fence, looking at Christopher Columbus, who, shaking and trembling in an ecstasy of pride, slowly paced towards us, his head almost buried so far did he throw it back.

"Aha," said the farmer, warmly.

We all climbed the fence. Christopher Columbus sidled away from us. We formed three lines of attack, like in the Battle of Crecy. We converged. Christopher Columbus, as light as a feather, leaped into the air and flew, with all the grace of a cow jumping a fence, to the top of the tool shed.

"One of you go up and get him," said the farmer. "I get lumbago stitches."

"If I go up," said Jim, "he's my bird."

So I went up. I reached for his leg, because, after all, his head was four feet away. As I touched the great sinewy beam of a leg, Christopher launched himself into space. The ladder wafted back, under the powerful heave of those wide wings. Sickeningly I arched backwards. Fair into Jim's rescuing arms.

"Talk about thanks!" gasped Jim.

And in a moment the farmer had walked up and captured poor Christopher Columbus, all exhausted by his aerial efforts.

"Heft him," said the farmer, lifting the giant creature over the fence to Jim. Jim took both hands.

"Here, help," said Jim.

So I took a part hold on those great legs, and patted the fat thighs exploratorily. What drum-sticks! What a mountain of white meat, above.

We marched into the yard and over to a block of stump wood. From its neat rack in the implement shed, the farmer brought a shining axe. Jim held the bird's feet. I held his head.

"Poor Christopher," cried the lady, throwing her apron over her head.

"A fine way," I said bitterly, closing my eyes and turning my face away, "to celebrate the fact that I never got hit with lightning."

"When I think," came the muffled voice of the lady, "of that poor soul on the next farm, wasting away."

"Pagans," muttered Jim. "That's all we are. Feasting."

I heard a sniffle and opened one eye to see the farmer, gripping the axe, covering his face with his hand.

"Here," I shouted. "If you feel that way about this poor bird!"

"Sciatica," muttered Jim, "stomach ulcers, phlebitis."

"One hail-storm," said the lady, "and where would we have been?"

I let go Christopher Columbus' bill. He flapped his wings furiously. Jim let go his feet. With a peep all out of proportion to his size, the huge bird floundered to the ground and with long strides and no dignity whatever he raced around the yard a couple of times to get his bearings and then legged it, head outstretched, down the lane.

So we went inside and sat talking about general debility and spots dancing before the eyes and so forth, including great storms of the past and plagues of cut-worms until it was time we were on our way, if we wanted a turkey before dark.

But up the lane, we met Christopher Columbus again, all puffed up and proud once more, his head pulled back, his wattles purple.

"Aw, heck," I said, "why not leave domestic matters to the women?"

Which we did.

Ginseng Hounds

June 18, 1938

"It's too hot," gasped Jimmie Frise, "for trout fishing and the bass season isn't open."

"The song birds," I agreed, "are too busy hunting worms for their young, to sing decently."

"All the best of the wild flowers," added Jim, "are through blooming."

"If we played golf," I said, as we sat on the edge of the trout stream in the shade of a cedar tree, "we could fill up all this part of the year very happily."

"No, the trouble with golf is," explained Jim, "that it steals away all a man's other recreations. Golf is a thief. Golf is the only thing there is to do in early April, so a man goes forth to this earliest amusement. And before he knows where he is, he is committed to a dozen pleasant golf engagements with friends. By the time he should be going fishing or taking his children into the wilds to hear the first songbirds or to see the first wild flowers blooming, the golf season is in full swing, and the poor devil can't disentangle himself from its insidious meshes."

"It's the easiest way, too," I agreed. "Here is a man faced with a week-end. He can either go out fishing or tramping in the woods or visit the summer resort in advance of the season. Or else he can slip out to the golf links and play golf. Of all the choices, golf appears the cheapest and handiest."

"Never let golf get us," said Jim, devoutly, and we sat

"Hey, mister," said the little boy, "aren't you scared?" "Scared of what?" I inquired from my kneeling position.

in silence in the fragrant cedar shade, while a catbird, its bill full of pale green worms, came secretly and looked at us, on its way to some hidden nest. In a moment, we heard it mew, and knew its young were fed.

"The great thing in life," said Jim, "is not to get entangled. Don't commit yourself to any belief or sect or sport or business. The essence of freedom is detachment."

"Most people," I disagreed, "are looking for an anchor. Most people love to be moored fast to the shore, instead of being adrift on the sea, calm or stormy."

In Tune With Nature

"Which is better?" inquired Jim, bravely, since we were safe in the sweet safety of a pleasant woods. "Which is better? To be wrecked at sea? Or to sink at the wharf, a decayed and rotted old hulk that has never even crossed the bay?"

"For," I added sententiously, "we all sink, in the end."

"You said it," confirmed Jim. "I would rather be sitting right here, in this idle glade, with the limpid stream barren of trout and no cow bells, even, to be heard, and no sense of activity or industry or improvement, no birds calling that we can pretend we are studying, no flowers to make us imagine ourselves amateur botanists—just sitting here, in utter idleness."

"Not even thinking," I pointed out.

"I often think," mused Jim, "that the Chinese are going to inherit the earth. They are the only race that seems in complete tune with nature. They have no great ambitions. They have only the ambitions that nature itself has, like these trees and that catbird and that stream. To live and grow and flow along. If storms come, fine. If the weather's fine, fine. But all the powers of man, in the past centuries of trying, have never succeeded in making the weather fine, if the weather wants to storm."

"But we've improved housing," I protested proudly, "and invented raincoats and cars and trains to keep us dry on our way to work. You can't say we haven't done something to make our lives more comfortable than a catbird's."

"I was speaking," said Jim, loftily, "in the allegorical sense. Unlike the Chinese, we have been trying for centuries to improve our physical life. With what result? That our world to-day is in greater confusion and terror and anxiety than ever before. It seems to be hovering eternally, day after day, year after year, on the brink of an immense precipice."

"Yeah," I said, "and where are the Chinese, may I ask?"

"Oh, they're suffering a little storm, at the moment," said Jim lightly. "But you know and I know and even the Japanese know, by now, that when the storm is spent, the Chinese will be there, as yesterday, today and forever, multiplying, living strangely and happily and slowly inheriting the earth."

"That gives me an idea," I said. "Let's hunt ginseng. Come on, let's walk through the woods here and hunt ginseng."

"You mean jinsin," corrected Jim, not getting up.

"Ginseng is its proper spelling," I informed him.

"Say, listen," scoffed Jim, "don't you try to tell me anything about jinsin. I was born on the farm. Lots of my neighbors grew big covered acres of jinsin. Why, every farm newspaper carried big advertisements about the fortunes that were to be made out of growing jinsin."

"Wild ginseng," I informed Jim, "is the only kind with magical properties."

The Root of Life

"Listen," laughed Jim, "I've seen all around our neighborhood, when I was a boy, big yards all roofed over with boards. There were posts stuck up every few feet, and the whole jinsin field roofed over with planks, with big cracks between, to let only a little sunlight in, just like in the deep forest where the jinsin grows."

"Call it ginseng, Jim," I insisted. "That's the way it is spelled in the Encyclopaedia Britannica, although the Chinese call it Jen Sheng, the root of life."

"All right," said Jim, "if the Chinese call it Jen Sheng and the encyclopaedia calls it ginseng, then I'll call it jinsin, which is what everybody called it up around my old home, and they grew it. So there."

"Jen Sheng," I said. "The root of life. The Chinese paid fabulous prices for the root of this wild plant. They paid as much as $3,000 for a forked root."

"They paid what?" said Jim, sitting up and almost standing up.

"They paid," I said, clearly, "as high as $3,000 for a good big forked root. Forked roots, which the Chinese thought looked like a man, have greater magical properties than plain roots. They restore youth. They lengthen life. They were the monkey glands of the Chinese, a thousand years ago."

"Where did you get all this?" demanded Jim, actually rising.

"In the encyclopaedia," I informed him. "Whenever I haven't anything else to do and it's raining, I go down and read the encyclopaedia. You'd be surprised at some of the things I've read."

"But $3,000," said Ji, grimly, gazing off into the leafy shadows of the woods around us.

"Ordinary ginseng," I said, "sells at around $5 a pound for the roots. They're sort of translucent, half-transparent, brittle. It takes years to grow a good root."

"All the years," muttered Jim, "that I lived right amongst all those fields full of jinsin."

"Ah, but the cultivated stuff," I explained, "doesn't command the price of the wild root. The Chinese find a far greater power in the wild root."

"Do you know what it looks like?" demanded Jim. "Would you know it if you saw it?"

"Jim," I said stiffly, "perhaps you forget that I am something of a botanist."

"Okay," said Jim, throwing off his creel and other useless gear. "Let's go look. What kind of ground does it grow on?"

So as we started to explore the woods, I explained to Jim in starts and fits of how ginseng grew in the deep woods, in shade and on high humus soil. I told him some of the legends of ginseng, and how the Chinese emperor, a thousand years ago, had to forbid the Chinese to search for it, because they were exterminating it from the whole of China, and it is a vast country. Ginseng hunters pushed back the borders of the Chinese empire. Into Manchuria and northern Siberia the ginseng hunters went, seeking the green treasure. I told him how it was discovered growing wild in America and how clever Americans began to cultivate it for the Chinese market. But how the Chinese were clever enough to know the cultivated from the wild root.

I explained that European doctors and pharmacologists had studied the root and found that it had no real virtues, but that it had a psychic value, since anything you believe in is as likely to help you as anything else. Far better than epsom salts, anyway.

And then we discovered, the ginseng. At least, I should say, I found it, because Jim's boyhood memories were pretty vague. All he could recollect were shadowy green jungles under plank roofs which the local farmers guarded with violent jealousy.

"Are you sure this is it?" asked Jim.

"Am I sure?" I scorned. "I tell you this is the genuine article. Look. I'll pull one up and show you the root."

I pulled tenderly, digging around the root with my fingers, and drew up out of the earth a queer, transparent, brittle root, about two inches long. And it was forked!

"Forked!" cried Jim. "My gosh, man, maybe you've just yanked up $3,000 by the roots."

He knelt and began digging furiously.

"Don't waste time," I explained, "taking the roots only. Take the whole plant and when we get an armful we can sit down and remove the roots."

So did we ever dig? And did we ever get some forked roots, Jim getting one nearly four inches long? And did we ever have an armful each when a little dog suddenly appeared out of the underbrush and began barking furiously at us?

And in a minute, did two little boys with fishing poles and freckles ever come out of the underbrush like groundhogs and stand staring speechless at us?

"Hey, mister," said the forwardest little boy, "ain't you scared?"

"Scared?" I inquired, from the kneeling position.

"Ain't you scared of poison ivy?" asked the child.

Jim dropped his armload violently.

"This," I said, leaping up, is not poison ivy, my son, this is ginseng."

"That ain't ginseng," said the little boy swallowing. "It's plain poison ivy, mister. You'll have spots all over you."

"Poison ivy," I stated firmly, "has shiny leaves and the leaves have a reddish color at the base of the leaf."

"Yeah, in the fall it has," agreed the little boy, tenderly, "but when it's young it hasn't. You'll have blisters everywhere, on your hands and arms and all over."

"I thought it was poison ivy," gasped Jim, his hands dangling far out for fear he would inadvertently touch his face. "I know poison ivy when I see it. That's poison ivy."

"Jim," I said.

"Come on," said Jim. "Let's get to the nearest drug store, quick. We can bath in soda or something."

So without even thanking the little boys, we went plunging through the woods and grabbed our tackle and hurried out the path to the car and, throwing everything in, started for town, the nearest town where there was a drug store being 11 miles.

The druggist was half asleep when we burst in but he came immediately to life when we explained that we had just submitted ourselves to serious infection from poison ivy.

"Look," I said, pointing to my chest, where there was already a slight rash.

Too Far To Go Back

Jim examined his chest and neck, and there was not only a rash but some little red spots already showing.

"Gents," said the druggist smartly, "step in to the back here; I've got a tub. I'll fix up a bath of ferric chloride and stuff and we'll see what can be done. But I'm afraid it's too late to allay the infection if you actually touched the stuff."

"Touched it?" groaned Jimmie.

And out in the back, while we peeled off to the waist,

the druggist ran a tub of water in a wooden washtub and dumped ferric chloride and glycerine, and Jim and I without ado plunged into the tub and slathered the stuff all over us. The druggist helped us, pouring additional little bottles of this and that into the tub as he recalled the various cures and antidotes to poison ivy. We sloshed and splashed and labored mightily, wasting no time for talk, until, as we had thoroughly saturated ourselves and had the water running down into our pants, the druggist inquired how we had got messed up with the poison ivy.

"It was ginseng we were looking for," I explained humbly. "I thought I knew ginseng when I saw it. We picked armfuls of it."

"There's lots of ginseng through here," admitted the druggist.

"Two kids came through the woods, with a little dog," I elucidated, "or else we would have carried armfuls of the stuff up against our faces and everything."

"Two little boys, with what color of a dog?" asked the druggist. "Whereabouts were you hunting?"

"Two concessions north and the sixth side road west," I explained, also going into details as to the little dog and the little boys, gratefully.

"Were these kids," asked the druggist, "freckled and did one of them do all the talking?"

"That's them," said Jim.

The druggist stepped forward and examined the rash on our chests and the red spots on Jimmie's neck.

"That's prickly heat," he said, "and that's mosquito bites. That's from over-exertion in the heat."

"Not poison ivy?" said Jim.

"No more poison ivy than I am," said the druggist. "And that was ginseng you had. And those two kids are the biggest ginseng hounds in the whole county. And they interrupted you pulling up one of their favorite beds of it, I suppose."

"Nnnn, nnn, nnn," said Jimmie and I.

But when we got dried up and everything, and paid the druggist for the bath, we decided it was too far to go back, and anyway the kids would be vanished by then, and besides, what could we do if we did find them?

Surprise
Party

"Good heavens," gasped
Laura . . . "What are you
doing here?"

March 25, 1939

"We're invited to a surprise party," announced Jimmie
Frise.

"At our age?" I protested.

"It's time we started taking back from the young people," declared Jim, "some of the things we've handed over to them."

"Surprise parties," I demurred, "never did appeal to me. Even in short pants."

"We've handed over everything to the kids," pursued Jim. "We have handed over authrority to them. They boss us now. We've given them our cars. We've admitted them to knowledge, so that the average kid of 15 knows more than his father."

"Let them keep the surprise parties," I pleaded, "and we'll take back our cars."

"At 10 years of age," went on Jim relentlessly, "we teach them in school the art of debate. So they can come home and confound us."

"Surprise parties," I insisted, "never surprise."

"Since I was a boy," propounded Jimmie, "a great revolution has occurred. We have handed over the world to childhood. It's time we cut out this sentimental nonsense and started to take back a little of life for ourselves. Let's start putting the kids in their place."

"By going to surprise parties?" I scoffed.

"Let's start stealing back," said Jim, "some of the fun that formerly belonged to children. Let's start by stealing their parties."

"Huh, huh," I laughed, "and play post-office?"

"The party we're invited to," informed Jim, "is at Bill McDoodle's."

"Bill McDoodle's," I cried. "That big shot? Why, we haven't hardly seen Bill in 15 years."

"He used to be our pal," said Jim.

"Yeah," I muttered, "until he started up in the world. Until he became a big executive with a capital B."

"Aw, well, for old-time's sake," said Jim.

"Listen," I stated, "the last 10 times I've seen Bill McDoodle, he hasn't known me. He looks at me with an expression of faint recollection and then decides he must have been mistaken—it wasn't me after all."

"Big business makes men that way," explained Jim.

"Big business my ear," I cried. "He used to be just one

of our gang. Then he got that vice-president job out of a blue sky. We were as pleased as he was. Don't you remember?"

"We staged a celebration for him," remembered Jimmie.

"And he didn't come," I recalled. "Inside of a year, if we ever ran into him anywhere, he was good-humoredly condescending, and chuckled over the old days. The old days, as if he had outgrown all that."

"Well, now he wants to recapture the old days," pleaded Jim.

"Let him chase them," I asserted. "They're hard to catch."

"Listen," wheedled Jim, "it's his wife invited us. You remember her? A mighty fine girl."

"Sure, I remember her," I agreed. "Many's the time I've lent her my coat. Yet one year after they'd gone up in the world, I spoke to her in the lobby of a theatre, all dolled up in an opera cloak, and she looked right past me."

A Pathetic Figure

"Look," said Jim, "I told her we'd come to her party. She actually begged us to come."

"I wonder if Bill's had a come-down?" I mused wickedly.

"It isn't that," explained Jim. "She told me just how it was. They've had their fill of society. Nothing gives them any pleasure any more. Bill is unhappy all day long and all night. He just sits, moody and glum. Business doesn't interest him. The clubs he belongs to sour him. His wife caught him last week up in the attic, looking at his old abandoned fishing tackle and guns, and he was sitting with his hip rubber boots on, up in the attic, his head buried in his hands."

"Huh, huh, huh," I laughed sympathetically.

"So she's decided to give him a big surprise," went on Jim. "She is going to stage a surprise party, and invite about 30 of the old friends they had 20 years ago. Friends of their youth. Not a single person they have met in the last 10 years, she said."

"Jim," I declared, "I don't see why we should accommodate them in this whim. Friends are too precious a possession to cast away. We've remained friends across all the years, with Bumpy and Vic and Skipper and all the lads. Some of us have got rich and some of us poor, but we've weathered all the years. We've retained something lovely and precious. Why should we let these people horn in on it?"

"Friendship," said Jim, "ought to be great enough to lift across a gap of years. They used to be our friends. In folly, they cast it away. Now they ask us to take them back. If our capacity for friendship is big enough, we'll take them back."

"The capacity for friendship, Jim," I informed him, "decreases with the years. When I was a boy, all boys were my friends. When I was a young man, I found I was narrowing down the field. By the time I was 30, I had pruned down my friends to a rough dozen, and I was beginning to be doubtful of some of them. I figure a man of 60 is lucky to have one friend."

"The party," said Jim, "is to be a surprise party and a hard times party."

"Good grief," I exclaimed. "They'll play post-office sure."

"We can dress up in old rags and goofy hats," enthused Jim, "and it won't be for our prosperous exterior that Bill will welcome us to his swell big house."

"He's got quite a house, I hear," I admitted.

"It's a mansion," assured Jim. "It must have cost him $50,000 and they say he gave an interior decorator $10,000 to furnish it."

"Yet he sits in the attic," I accused, "with his head in his hands."

"That's what comes," pointed out Jim, "of letting somebody else plan your home. The home a man loves is the home he has assembled piece by piece, item by item, picture by picture. You are never lonely in a home that you have built little by little, because wherever your eye rests, you see something of yesterday. And yesterday is all that appeals to a man after he reaches the age when tomorrow makes him afraid."

"You're trying to make him out quite a pathetic figure," I said.

"He is a pathetic figure," said Jim. "And even if it is only for the mean satisfaction of showing him how happy and carefree you are, how full of friends and life, you ought to come to the party."

"When is it?" I inquired.

"Thursday night," said Jim.

"Thursday's a big night on the air," I pointed out. "I like to sit at home Thursdays."

"If the party bores you," said Jim, "I know you well enough to know that you'll go and turn the radio on and sit there like a bump on a log."

"It isn't my manners that have kept me my friends," I agreed heartily.

"Can I count on you?" asked Jim eagerly.

"Okay," I said. "I like to get inside a rich man's house now and then, just for a quiet smile."

So we spent a while planning our hard times costumes. It is a little difficult in these days to get together a real hard times outfit. Your wife has given everything away. But I remembered a straw hat that hung on a nail in the cellar, and Jim recalled a derby, greenish with age, that some previous owner of his house had left on the fruit shelves. If I wasn't mistaken, my mother-in-law had kept an old cutaway coat, vintage of about 1890, which was a relic of far-off romance, which she trotted out on festive occasions along with a great gray lustre ball gown of hers, trimmed with black velvet. I figured I could borrow the cutaway, and enhance it with a frayed shirt. Jim had a pair of faded overalls in the back of his car which he used for duck hunting.

"We'll manage," he assured me.

And when Thursday came, we managed all right. In the straw hat and greenish old cutaway, and a pair of antique tan boots we found in a trunk, I cut a peculiarly disgusting figure. And Jim, in the derby, and overalls and a bedraggled old sweater coat he borrowed from the furnace man, looked like something fallen off a freight train.

"There," shouted Jim, when I called for him, "doesn't that take you back 30 years?"

"I was just thinking we looked pretty average," I said, "considering the times."

So we drove from the modest neighborhood where we live up, up, into an ever more refined region, where the corner drugstores got farther and farther apart and presently there were no more stores at all, but just dark and gloomy houses. By a lot of peering, we finally located Bill's street and eventually his house, set back from the neighbors. We looked at our watch.

"Right on the nose," said Jim, parking. "Nine p.m."

The house seemed quiet. There were a few other cars parked about.

"Let's wait for the gang," I suggested.

"No, Laura said she'd meet us and steer us into a downstairs room," said Jim. "Come on."

We walked respectfully up the handsome steps and rang the bell. A uniformed maid opened.

"What is it?" she asked sharply.

"We have an appointment with Mrs. McDoodle," said Jim, stepping in.

The maid looked us over shrewdly and pointed to an oak bench in the hall. She flounced her skirts at us and went upstairs.

The house was deathly silent. Footsteps pattered above and then down the grand staircase came Laura.

"Good heavens!" she gasped, halting and throwing her hand to her mouth.

"What?" said Jim and I, rising smartly to our feet.

"What are you doing here?" hissed Laura, leaping down the stairs and glaring at us fiercely.

"The party?" smiled Jim thinly.

"The party's tomorrow night," hissed Laura, starting to shove us towards the door, the little maid standing bravely behind her.

"I thought you said Thursday night," said Jim, all muddled and trying to recover us both.

178

"I said Friday night," cried Laura, brokenly. "Now you'll ruin it all."

"Sssshhh," said Jim.

For heavy footsteps came from above.

"What is it?" called down Bill in a melancholy voice.

"Nothing, dear, nothing," said Laura, wildly jockeying us to the door.

But down the stairs came Bill and saw his wife trying to shoo two tramps out the door.

"Hey, wait a minute," shouted Bill, hurrying.

"Oh," moaned Laura.

"Why," gasped Bill, when he recognized us. "Why . . . Laura . . . these are old friends. Why, it's Jim. And Greg. Why . . ."

And he came and took our arms and looked with horror-stricken eyes into our faces and down at our clothes.

Behind him danced Laura, her finger on her lips, signalling us frantically.

"Why, boys," said Bill, with a husky voice, "Why, my dear boys."

And gripping our elbows fiercely, he steered us back through the handsome hall and into a little den, all lined with leather and books. He shoved us in, shut the door on poor Laura who was dancing desperately behind us.

"Laura," said Bill, a little sharply, "if you don't mind, I'll just see the boys alone."

He shut the door gently on her.

He shoved chairs out for us, with pathetic eagerness. He tried his hardest not to look at us, but we could see his shocked glance furtively taking in our ragged clothes, our shapeless boots, the silly hats we carried.

"Cigars," he said hoarsely, with trembling hands reaching for a walnut box. "Cigars, boys . . ."

Suddenly he halted. Pulled himself up. Tightened his jaws and then stared us square in the face.

"Bill," began Jim, slightly hysterical.

"Boys," cried Bill, holding his hand up commandingly. "This is a very, very strange thing. I've been thinking of you fellows for weeks. I tell you it's an answer to my prayers to see you here."

"Bill . . ." I began, trying not to snort with laughter.

"Please," begged Bill, brokenly, "please, let me have my say. It's a pitiful thing, but let me say it. Boys, for years I've been lonelier than in hell. For months I have been wondering what was the matter with me, life had gone sour. For weeks, I have been actually thinking of you two, and Vic and Bump and Skipper and all. I've been praying, do you hear . . . praying that I could find some decent way of discovering the friends I used to have . . . before I . . . before . . ."

He looked at us and we at him, and of all the dreadful sights in the world, if there weren't tears tumbling down Bill's face.

"I didn't know," he said, in his nose, "I didn't know, God be my witness, that you had come on tough times. God be my witness. Nobody ever told me. You'd think, somebody would have told me. But why should anybody tell me? And Laura trying to shove you out of my house."

He glared at us through his tears.

"Boys," he said, "anything I've got is yours. You can have anything in the world you want of me. Why didn't you come to me sooner? I've been so damn lonely. So damn lonely."

And Bill suddenly leaped forward and grabbed for our hands, and began, for the first time, boldly to look close at our faded rags, our cheap and ragged shirts, at Jim's horrible soggy sweater coat.

"But, Bill," said Jim, after several twists of his neck to find his voice, "Bill, it's all right. We don't want anything. We just came to call on you."

"It's a miracle," said Bill passionately. "A miracle."

But Laura had been listening at the keyhole, the way those rich women do; and she pushed the door open and looked with a white face at Bill and us; and then she said: "Jim, what did I tell you?"

So we all had to sit down quietly while Laura and Jimmie and I patiently explained to Bill all about the surprise party and how we, as usual, had got the dates mixed. And how, therefore, Bill had been trapped into revealing something more surprising than any surprise party.

And we stayed until 1 o'clock Friday morning; and Friday night, when the whole 30 of us came, was it ever a surprise party, to them and to Bill and to us and all the old friends who meet sooner or later.

Bats Where!

April 1, 1939

Suddenly something fluttered out from the planks. "A bat!" I shouted. "Where?" demanded Jim.

"If anything makes me sick," declared Jimmie Frise, "it's spring housecleaning."

"The law ought to be," I agreed, "that spring housecleaning had to be done on and not before May first. Then it would coincide with the opening of the trout season."

"Perfect, perfect," cried Jim. "Then the men could all go trout fishing for three or four days and leave the women to their frenzy."

"Personally," I submitted, "I can't see the use of spring cleaning. It makes no difference. They're always sweeping and dusting and using the vacuum anyway. They never rest. I think it is a kind of a spring disease in women like trout fishing or gardening with men."

"I wouldn't doubt that at all," said Jim. "They go kind of nuts, don't they? They get all flushed and a wild look in their eyes?"

"It's a form of spring fever," I assured Jim. "Nature gives us all these deep instincts, like falling in love in June and feeling very industrious and saving in September, in order to keep us alive and going. This spring cleaning business probably dates away back to the cave man. I bet the caves were in a mess by the time spring came."

"Old gnawed bones, and ashes and everything," agreed Jim.

"So all the females of the cave man species," I followed, "were suddenly filled with a furious fever of energy and they got to work and held a kind of bone flinging and ash chucking orgy, to clean out the cave. It's the same thing as in a wren, when she returns to the bird house in our gardens. She goes mad flinging out all the old sticks and debris of last year's nests. If nature sends a lady wren nutty, there is no reason why it shouldn't work with women."

"Yet, the pity of it is," said Jim, "that this fever isn't necessary any more. Women keep homes clean all the year around, every day, sometimes twice a day. All this rumpus is sheer nuisance."

"You can't reason with them," I warned.

"Naturally," said Jim. "You can't reason with a man in fever delirium. That's what it is, spring delirium."

"Do you think," I asked, "we could talk it over with them and get them to put it off until May first?"

"So we could go fishing until it's over?" mused Jim.

"It's a perfect arrangement," I submitted.

"Yeah," muttered Jim, "but there's one little difficulty. My family has got me in a corner. They have it all arranged that I am to clean up the attic."

"Do that in advance," I cried. "Get it over with."

"I might do that," admitted Jim.

"It isn't the work that upsets men," I explained. "It's the way the whole house is thrown into a wreck for nearly a week. That's what gets a man's goat. I don't mind a little work."

Antipathy To a Broom

"Would you help me with my attic?" inquired Jim.

"Why not?" I retorted. "What's the trick about your attic?"

"Well, in a way," said Jim, "the attic is mine, you see? All my stuff is up there. Guns, fishing tackle, decoys, work-bench. I've got that old work bench up there. I've been tinkering at making decoys and things and there's a lot of shavings and sawdust."

"Aaaaah," I said.

"That's why the women insist on me cleaning it up," explained Jim. I promised I'd clean it up last year. And the year before, I agreed to, and I did clean it up in a kind of a way. But they say it is my job and this year they're kind of ganged up on me."

"Of course, what you could do," I offered, "is let it go to the bitter end and then one day you'll come home and find they've done it in desperation."

"They can't," said Jim. "I've got the key. I keep the attic locked ever since the days the kids were small. I didn't want them going up and messing around my tackle and guns and stuff."

"And you don't want them messing around there now?" I added.

"Certainly not," said Jim. "Even downstairs, where things are organized, I can never find anything I want after spring cleaning. It takes me about six weeks to get the house reorganized after spring cleaning. But if they ever got up into my attic, good heavens, I might never find anything again, ever."

"I guess it's up to you," I sighed.

"I'm afraid it is." said Jim. "The sawdust and shavings and things sometimes drift down through the cracks under the door. They are even saying that the sawdust is seeping through the ceilings. A man by rights ought to have a little cabin down at the foot of his yard, shouldn't he?"

"After his kids start to grow up," I agreed, "a man's house is no longer his castle. It becomes only a sort of checker-board on which he plays a steadily losing game."

"It was good of you to offer to come and help me with the attic," felt out Jim.

"Not at all," I said, "providing it's not some night I can't get away."

"Oh, I'll let you pick the night," said Jim; which is a pretty low trick.

"I'm not particularly good at domestic work," I submitted. "In fact, I have been told I am more a nuisance than a help."

"Don't you believe it," cried Jim, heartily. "You're a tidy little fellow. You can sweep while I shift the bigger stuff around."

"H'm," said I, neither positive nor negative, because there is some deep antipathy in my nature to a broom. Maybe some of my ancestors were stable boys.

To Clean Up the Attic

At any rate, Jim referred in a casual way to the cleaning of his attic from day to day, and finally, he tricked me.

"Did you hear about that short newsreel picture about bird dogs?" Jim inquired sweetly.

"No, where is it? I asked.

"It's at some theatre on Bloor St.," said Jim. "I'll look it up. It shows bird dogs pointing quail, and the gunners walking up to the point and flushing the birds and making lefts and rights. Boy, they say it is one of the most wonderful sport pictures ever produced."

"Let's go tonight," I said promptly.

"Can you get off tonight?" asked Jim, pointedly.

"This is the first night I've got to myself in a week," I assured him.

So Jim got up and pretended to hunt through the theatre ads for the picture and couldn't find it. Then he telephoned one of the movie exchanges, and they said the picture wouldn't be showing in the local theatres for another month.

"I must," said Jim, innocently, "have seen the ad somewhere else. But say, look here, if you're free tonight, how about coming over and giving me a hand with that attic of mine."

"Er," I said.

"Let's get it over and done with. It's only a month to the fishing seaon. You wouldn't want me tied up with a lot of house-cleaning on May the first?" demanded Jim.

And since I couldn't think of any graceful excuse, I was roped.

"It's a perfect night for it," continued Jim. "The family is all going to be out. We can have the house to ourselves. If we find any short cuts, we can use them, with nobody around."

"Like chucking shavings, et cetera, out the attic window," I instanced.

So waiting until around 8 o'clock to allow Jim's family to leave the house and also to allow my supper to settle, I strolled around to Jim's and he led me without delay upstairs and via the little stairway into the attic, which is just one big unfinished room, perfectly suited to a man's needs.

It was a mess. No wonder Jim kept the attic door locked and the key in his pocket. One corner was full of decoy ducks, like coal heaped in a coal bin. Another corner had an enormous heap of what appeared to be old magazines, hunting coats, rubber boots and fish baskets. In the midst stood a small carpenter's work bench, and a foot deep all around it lay a drift of shavings, sawdust, hunks of wood, and all the ingredients of a fine life devoted to making things of no particular value or success.

"Well, Jimmie," I said, "quite an evening's work."

"Now," said Jim, very energetic. "I've got it figured out. I'll start shifting everything to a new place, like, and you follow me with the broom."

"If your wife," I said, "ever saw this place."

"I've been scared stiff this last few months," admitted Jim. "Haunted, by day and by night."

I peeled off my coat and hung it on a nail. Jim handed me the broom.

"I'll start here, with these decoys," suggested Jim. "I'll shift them all over to that corner, and you sweep. Then when you catch up to me, I'll shift the decoys and what will be under them to another corner, and so on. We'll keep going around and around, see, until it is all cleaned up."

"That's the way the women do," I admitted. Shift everything around."

So Jim started picking up big armfuls of decoys and carting them to the next corner, and to fill in the time, I started batting with the broom at the dusty rough, unfinished planking and rafters of the attic wall and ceiling.

Suddenly, in the garish light of the naked electric light bulb, something fluttered out from the planks.

"A bat," I shouted.

Jim dropped an armful of ducks and peered into the already dusty glare of light.

"Where?" he demanded.

We stood perfectly still, and heard a small scratching sound.

"Here," I said, swinging the broom.

The bat leaped heavily into space and wobbled sleepily around, narrowly missing our heads.

"Swing it," roared Jim, snatching up a long piece of scantling that lay in the debris on the floor.

I swung. The bat ducked. I ducked; the bat swung.

"Look out," shouted Jim, charging for the narrow stairway. "It'll get downstairs."

But he was too late. The bat, attracted perhaps by the warm current of air coming up the attic stairway, followed down, and we were just in time to see it wobble on half-wakened wings, into the glow of light at the foot of the attic stairs.

"After it," commanded Jimmie, fiercely. "The women would go crazy if they saw that bat in the house."

Riot and Confusion

Down the stairs we thundered and commenced a cautious search, in room after room, listening, holding our breath, waiting to hear the faint scratching of the bat hiding behind some picture or mirror.

"Prod around," said Jim.

So we prodded around, shoving at pictures on the wall, shifting dressers and keeping a wary eye.

"Turn on the bright lights," I commanded, "blind the beast."

Suddenly, soundlessly, the little bat came staggering and wobbling along the hallway ceiling and darted into the room.

Jim swung. The chandelier crashed terribly and splintered glass flew in all directions. The bat darted out.

"After it!" shouted Jim, colliding his hunk of scantling along walls and doors.

I heard another violent crash. Jim had swung at the bat in the front bedroom and swiped all the ornaments off the top of a chest of drawers.

"Downstairs," cried Jim, leading the chase.

"Be careful," I begged. "Don't wreck the house."

"Better wreck the house than have that bat in it when the folks get home," gasped Jimmie, crouched and searching like a gangster in a movie.

We found the bat after we had disarranged all the pictures in the living room and shifted all the furniture and upset everything on the buffet. It was up in the chandelier.

"Poke with your broom," whispered Jim. "Poke it out towards me."

Jim poised like a baseball player, gripping the scantling mightily.

I poked with the broom at the poor little beastie. It fluttered out towards Jim.

Jim swung. The chandelier swayed madly tinkled into a thousand splinters of glass and then, slowly losing its wiry grip of the ceiling, came down with about a square foot of plaster.

"I missed," moaned Jim.

"Like heck you did," I said, from my shelter under the dining-room table.

The house was full of dust, riot and confusion.

"Where did it go?" I begged.

"I saw it go upstairs again," said Jim wearily.

So we followed. After 10 minutes, we found it under the bath-tub. It eluded us again, and to our joy, it turned up the attic stairs again.

"Good," said Jim. "Now we've got it on our own territory."

So we went after it, and got into Jim's private attic just in time to see the bewildered little creature alight flat against the rough beams of the ceiling and tuck itself cleverly and quickly in behind some great two-inch stringers of the roof.

"Aaaaah," sighed Jim. "Leave him there. Leave him right there, still in his winter sleep, the little devil, and some nice spring evening, I'll open the window and let him fly out."

"It's best to leave a bat alone," I agreed. "Just let him fly away."

"He sure has wasted the evening," said Jim.

"We'd better quit this job," I offered, "and go down and straighten things up the best way we can before the folks get back."

So we turned the light off, carefully locked the door, went down and telephoned the drug store for a couple of dozen new light bulbs, and straightened all the pictures and dusted everything, and did the best we could with the fallen chandelier.

"There'll be the dickens to pay," I said, after we had worked for an hour and still everything looked disturbed, somehow.

"It'll give them a taste," said Jim, "of what we men have to suffer when they're spring cleaning."

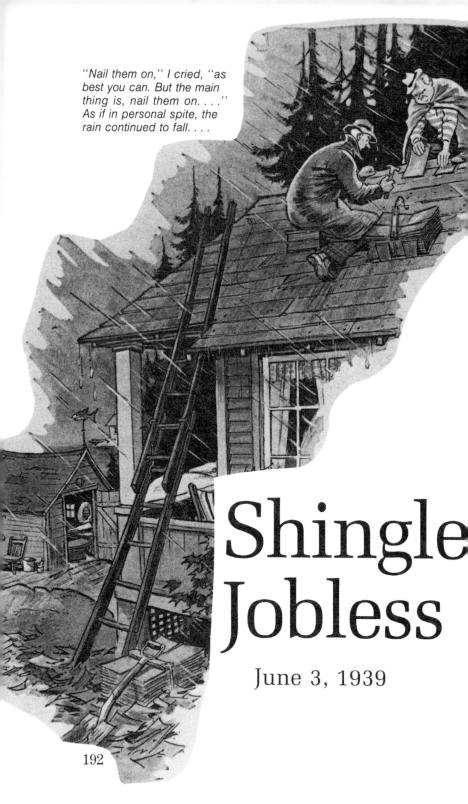

"Nail them on," I cried, "as best you can. But the main thing is, nail them on. . . ."
As if in personal spite, the rain continued to fall. . . .

Shingle
Jobless

June 3, 1939

"Life," said Jimmie Frise, "usually boils down to a question of dollars and cents."

"Never," I asserted.

"What I mean," said Jim, "is most decisions we make are dependent more on what it costs than what it means."

"Not me," I declared.

"Well, you take a rich man," said Jim. "The fact that he is rich ought to be a sort of reassurance to him that he has the stuff it takes to be successful. He shouldn't worry about losing even all his money. He ought to know that if he goes broke he would never need to starve."

"Men don't get rich," I assured, "by holding any such silly notions."

"The richer they get," pursued Jim, "the meaner they get. Nine-tenths of the squawks before courts of revision in regard to taxes aren't from the poor. They're from the rich. And the loudest roars come from the richest people."

"Poor people," I explained, "have no faith in squawking."

"Who is it," demanded Jimmie, "that complains most about income taxes? The rich."

"Naturally," I agreed, "because they have to pay most."

"Yes, but look what they have left after they have paid," said Jim. "A millionaire may have to pay a quarter of a million, but he has three-quarters of a million left."

"To get a million dollars," I explained, "you have to develop special instincts. Working hard is not enough. Anybody can work hard. Nobody works harder than most men who earn $15 a week. But to make a million, you have to develop a point of view. You have to get rid of a great many of the nicest things you own, like laziness and indifference and tolerance and the sweet laissez faire of life."

"Laissez who?" inquired Jim.

"Laissez faire," I explained, "is a French expression meaning let 'er ride. To make a million dollars, you have to let no single minute ride. You have to dress yourself each morning in a sort of tights. You have to trim your days down, minute by minute, to the cold, hard stalk, like celery. You have to concentrate yourself, like a dog at point. To go efficient and cold and devout for one day is not enough. You have to endure it for weeks. And months. And years."

"Some of the meanest guys I ever knew," said Jim, were men just like you describe, and they hadn't a cent and they were miserable."

"Well, to tell you the truth," I agreed, "the same rules make some men rich and some men paupers."

"Then where do we get off?" demanded Jim.

"We don't get off," I rejoiced. "Life never lets us off. It is like a symphony orchestra. Some men have to work like the devil, in the front row, and fiddle like mad and make all the loveliest noise. And others saw away in the background, making a few sounds with long silences in between. And some of them hit the triangle or the drum three times in the whole evening. But we are all necessary to the tune."

Needing 14 Dishpans

"That's a heck of a philosophy," declared Jim.

"Think of a better one," I submitted.

"I like to think, said Jim, "that a man gets what he deserves."

"That he reaps what he sows?" I suggested.

"Exactly," said Jim. "That's the way it ought to be."

"That is the way it is!" I triumphed. "The man with money reaps money. The man with brains and ideas reaps the fruit of his ideas. And the great mass of mankind reaps nothing but a bare living."

"I wish," said Jim, "the rich guys and the people with brains and ideas didn't reap so much."

"How much taxes did you pay last year?" I inquired. "At $10,000 a mile, how many miles of highway did you build?"

"I . . . ah . . ." said Jim.

"How many miles of highway did you travel over last year?" I demanded.

"I . . . ah . . ." said Jim.

"Exactly," I crowed.

"The thing that bothers me," said Jimmie, as if to clear the air, "is the roof on my summer cottage. It has to be shingled this year."

"Shingle it, then," I concurred.

"I haven't the money," sighed Jim.

"Okay, don't shingle it," I advised.

"It leaks so badly," stated Jim, "we have to buy three new dishpans every summer to attend to the new leaks. There are five leaks in the living room, three in the main bedroom, two in both the other bedrooms and three in the kitchen. How many dishpans is that?"

"Fourteen," I added.

"No summer cottage," declared Jim, "is entitled to 14 dishpans. I can't send my family up, the way it is. I haven't the money to repair the roof. There is only one solution."

"Which is?" I asked.

"Rent it," said Jim. "I can rent it for $150 for the season, which is just the amount I require to buy the shingles and have it re-roofed."

"How about the tenants?" I inquired.

"There will be sufficient dishpans," said Jim, "to look after the tenants."

"Do you mean to say," I inquired, "that you would deliberately rent your cottage to strangers for the purpose of raising enough money to make the cottage habitable for yourself?"

"People who rent cottages," said Jim, "don't expect much."

"They don't expect to get flooded out," I declared.

"We property owners," stated Jim, "can't afford to be finicky."

"Finicky is a trick word," I countered. "If you are cold-bloodedly going to rent your summer cottage for the purpose of raising enough dough to shingle it, I think you are verging on the shady."

"Look," said Jimmie. "Do you think for one minute that I would rent the view, the prospect, from my summer veranda for $150? Does anybody else think I would? Do you imagine that I would surrender that beautiful lake, that lovely hill behind my place, filled with maples and birches, for a measly $150? Is it conceivable that a man who for 15 years has loved that summer home far more than all the cities he has lived in, the apple of his eye, the object of all his dreams in bleak December and vicious February, would forego it for a lousy $150?"

"So what?" I cut in.

"Anybody that rents a summer place for $150," insisted Jim, "expects leaks in the roof.

"A Child Could Do It"

"I don't agree with you," I submitted coldly.

"What a moralist you are," sneered Jim.

"All I say is," I stated, "if you love your summer place so much, why don't you shingle it?"

"Because I haven't $150," said Jim.

"Do you realize," I inquired, "how simple shingling is? Don't you know that all you have to do is take a common garden spade and shovel the shingles off? There, revealed before you, are the rough planks of the roof."

"You seem to have done some shingling," admitted Jim.

"Only two years ago," I said, "I shingled our boathouse. You shovel all the old shingles off. They make a grand pile of kindling. Then, on the planks, you nail, starting from the bottom, row after row of shingles. You can't go wrong."

"Don't tell me," said Jim. "I've shingled whole barns. Whole barns."

"You lay a row of shingles along the bottom," I stated. "Then you lay the next row. You can't go wrong. Two nails in each shingle. You can, if you like, stretch a chalk line and mark the position of each row in advance."

"It's not so simple," averred Jim.

"A child could do it," I scoffed.

"How long would it take?" inquired Jim.

"You could do it on a week-end," I encouraged.

"Would you come up this next week-end?" he asked.

"It's no affair of mine," I protested. "I have my own shingling to do in case I ever get a leak."

"It is your affair," corrected Jim. "You point out the moral aspect of the thing to me. You forbid me to rent my cottage to make enough to pay for the job."

"I am only your friend," I pointed out. "A friend can help you from making a false step that you might regret."

"But a friend can't help me do a little shingling?" mused Jim.

"It's so simple," I assured. "You could do it yourself in one day."

But the trouble with being a moralist is that it gets you tangled up in all sorts of involuntary activities. Jim ordered seven squares of cedar shingles and the keg of nails. Each of us brought the garden spade with us, besides our fishing rods. And Friday afternoon we drove to Bracebridge and into Jim's place which for a fact is beautiful. The shingles were mouldy and rotted, moss grew on them and there were all kinds of signs inside the cottage of the leaks which were beyond all patching. We counted eleven leaks Jim knew of and five new ones.

And on the beautiful Saturday morning under a lucid June sky we rose early and donned our working clothes which are our fishing clothes, and up ladders we swarmed to the soggy roof and with our spades made short work of the shingles.

They were old and all too ready to relax from their job of trying to shelter the cottage beneath. The nails were all rusty. The shingles were curled and brittle and mossy. With one swipe of the spade you could remove a square yard of them.

"This is going to be pie," said Jim, as we shovelled the decayed shingles off the roof into great drifts along the cottage sides.

The boards underneath, the roof proper, were somewhat decayed in spots, and I pointed out to Jim that the weak spots occurred where the shingles had been neglected.

And by eleven o'clock we had every shingle off and all the rusty nails jerked out with a deft twist of the spade.

Down around the cottage, unsightly piles of the old shingles lay.

"After lunch," said Jim, "we'll hoist up a package of shingles and start on the shingling. Meantime, let us relax and have a nice lunch."

"The hard part is behind us," I agreed. "From now on, a nice orderly job awaits. We ought to have it done by sundown."

As If All Were Ordained

So we climbed down off the roof and rested awhile, having a smoke and a nice long gaze out over the lake and a listen to all the merry notes of the nesting birds about. And then we started the fire and cooked ourselves a dish of canned spaghetti and laid out the radishes and green onions our families had provided, and the cold fried bacon and the loaf of crusty French bread. And we had a fine lunch, with strong tea of the kind you never get at home because they are afraid to put enough tea in the pot.

And after a hearty crunchy luncheon of the kind a man likes, we left the dishes and went for a stroll down by the lake and sat for a little on Jimmie's rustic bench and leaned back and stretched our muscles, cramped a little with stooping to the shovel.

"Yaw," yawned Jim, "a little snooze, hey?"

And snoozed at once; and I, after a few minutes, watching him, drowsed a moment, until I was waked by a growl.

"Hey," I cried. For the sky was black as ink and the lake was still as a mill pond and there was the echo of a thunderclap in the air.

"Good grief," gasped Jim, leaping up.

And we hurried to the cottage and Jim tore the flat metal bindings off a package of shingles with a hammer and handed them up the ladder to me in handfuls, because a bundle weighs too much for amateurs. And I tossed them hither and thither on the roof boards. And in no time, we were at the job, with pocketfuls of shingle nails.

"Nail them on," said Jim, "as best you can. But the main thing is, nail them on."

But in a gathering silence, the darkness increased, the rumbles grew, and quite finally, as if all were ordained, the first great big splatters of rain hit the boards, making vast damp spots on the wood that had not tasted damp for many a long year.

As if in personal spite, the rain fell on us. I could distinctly see that on the roof of the next adjoining cottage it fell far more lightly than it fell on ours. Special deluges seemed aimed at us. Wiping, curving deluges, intent and deliberate.

"Cover the cracks," shouted Jim, above the roar of the rain and the rumble of the thunder. It came and it went. It thinned and thickened. We lost all plan. We gave up all idea of laying the shingles in even rows. We just tacked them furiously over the cracks and knot holes.

"It's no use," said Jim, blowing raindrops off his nose tip. "Let's go down and cover up what we can inside."

So we slid down the ladder and went indoors, to find every crack in the roof pouring fringes of water down, and we seized mattresses and bent them into bundles to hide under tables; and we set dishpans, of which Jimmie has several, to catch the water spouts. And the cushions and the couches and the chairs with upholstery we upturned, in most cases too late; and then we went into the clothes closet, which has a separate roof within the roof, and there we sat and had a damp smoke and looked forlornly out into the living room and listened to the sound of rain not on the roof but on the floor.

"Who suggested this?" demanded Jim.

"Don't look at me," I retorted. "This is a judgment on you for even thinking of renting your cottage to strangers."

"It goes to show you," said Jim, "what comes of trying to save money."

So after the rain passed and a soft dripping afternoon broke sweetly, like a little child after a crying fit, we got in the car and went down and dickered with the man in the village who supplies the milk and builds the docks and cuts down the dead trees, and he came back up with us and inspected the situation and set a price of $27 for the job, seeing as how we had the shingles delivered and on the spot.

Jim limbered up with the baseball bat, in readiness. "You've got to be ready for fast work," I cautioned him, "because when they come they may come in a bunch."

Aw, Rats

December 2, 1939

"What," inquired Jimmie Frise, "do you know about rats?"

"Rats," I informed him, "are my meat. What I don't know about rats isn't in the encyclopaedia. I have killed thousands of rats. Black rats, gray rats, brown rats, fat rats. In the army they called me the Pie-Eyed Piper."

"There are rats," stated Jim, "under my garage. They've tunnelled down under the concrete floor. You can see the two entrances. From this dugout they come at night and forage in the garbage cans of the neighborhood. Members of the family coming home at night see them scuffling. They are huge."

"It will be no trick to get rid of them," I assured Jim. "You can use traps, poison, fumigation or a ferret. Maybe a ferret would be the best fun."

"I was thinking of sitting up some night," said Jim, "with a pleasant companion, both of us armed with .22 rifles. I thought we might spend a very amusing evening popping off rats."

"It would bring back the old days," I admitted fondly. "Many's the long night, in the war, I have whiled away potting rats with my revolver. I often thought that officers carried revolvers for no other purpose but rat shooting."

"Gosh," mused Jim, "did you ever see so many rats as we had in France, especially around the Vimy sector?"

"There were millions," I agreed. "Great big scaly-tailed brutes as big as tomcats."

"You might say," said Jim, "that after dark you could look in any direction, at any spot on the ground, and within one minute a rat was sure to cross that spot."

"They got so plentiful," I submitted, "and so bold, that they no longer confined their activities to the night. They moved freely about all over the place in broad daylight."

"And why not?" said Jim. "Nobody disturbed them. They had that vast silent world to themselves, especially by day. No human stirred. No man showed a head. It was at night that rats had to take care. At night we humans were abroad. We shared the night with the rats."

"As soon as night fell, in the trenches," I told, "and all the sentries were posted and all the working parties detailed, an officer had little to do but walk up and down and see that all was well. So presently he would pick a suitable spot, a bit of trench or a sap preferably near an old ruined house or barn. And there, sitting on the fire-step of the trench, he would unlimber his revolver and wait."

"So that," cried Jimmie, "was what all the shooting was about? We artillery used to sit away back with our guns, wondering what you gallant infantrymen were doing all the popping at."

"Mostly it was rats," I admitted. "I used to sit in the dark, motionless. In a few minutes, along the trench, on the parapet or from a rat hole in the wall of the trench, out would come a rat, secret, silent, sliding his head down, his back arched, seeking, sniffing. Quietly, the revolver comes up. Bang."

"You must have made an awful mess of them with that army gat," said Jim.

Dugout "Fishing" Trip

"If we hit them," I provided. "The best way of hitting a rat was known as fishing for rats. It was mostly done in old dugouts that were rat-infested. When it became so bad that the boys could not sleep owing to the rats running over them and fighting and squeaking all over the place, the boys would declare a fishing trip. All the men in the dugout would leave their snug beds on the damp cold planks of the dugout floor and go and sit on the stairways of the entrances. Then the expert would extinguish all the candles stuck along the plank walls and sit on the floor. Extending his legs, he would rest his rifle on his legs, the muzzle resting between the toes of his boots. Out from the end extended the bayonet; and on the end of the bayonet a piece of cheese would be impaled. There in the dark the fisherman sat, finger on trigger. When he felt a nibble on the cheese he fired. Seven times out of ten he blew the rat against the far wall of the dugout."

"Rather nasty," muttered Jim.

"What were sanitary corporals for?" I retorted.

"You wouldn't get many that way," said Jim.

"The rats were so plentiful and so greedy," I assured him, "that no sooner was one rat blown to pieces and the candles doused and the fisherman in position again before the rats, with a secret, soft, scuffling sound and squeaks and scutters, would be coming from their holes again amidst the planks of the dugout walls and ceilings, snuffling for that cheese. I have seen Corporal Cutsey Smith, now with God, get one dozen rats in one hour by this method."

"But it was a hopeless business," submitted Jim.

"It was," I agreed. "And I have often wondered since how France and Belgium got rid of all those countless rats after the war. It must have been one of the major post-war problems."

"When I close my eyes and try to recall what dugouts

were like," said Jim, "I can smell the queer sour smell of them, and the smell of coke gas and wood smoke. I can see again the dimness, the quietness, the men lying in their matted gray blankets and greatcoats on the muddy plank floors; see the two or three sitting up awake, in dim candlelight, writing letters; but most of all I can feel the silence, amidst which, ever and always, goes on the quiet scuffling and scratching of the rats behind the plank walls and ceilings, a sound that went on day and night."

"I woke up one night," I said, "with two rats fighting furiously on my chest."

"I have had a rat," countered Jim, "exploring in the dark come to me, lying on the ground, and place his two hands on the bridge of my nose to look over."

"Ugh," I surrendered. "What puzzles me is, if men hate rats so badly, how is it we haven't exterminated them ages ago, like all the other animals we hated and killed off?"

"I figure," said Jim, "there is a family of six rats under my garage."

"Right," I agreed. "The problem is how can we deal with the present situation. I suggest poison."

"Too many dogs in the neighborhood," said Jimmie. "I would sooner put up with rats than poison a dog."

"We can pump gas down the hole," I suggested. "Put a tube from the exhaust pipe of your car and carbon monoxide them."

Plan of Battle

"Wouldn't you kind of like to sit up tonight with .22 rifles, and do a little shooting?" wheedled Jim.

"It's too risky," I declared. "And too cold."

"Very well, a ferret then," said Jim. "Let's get some fun out of this. I don't like the idea of putting poison or fumes down the hole and letting them quietly die down under the concrete floor of the garage. They might smell. I'd like to get a whack at them. And a ferret would chase them out and we could stand at the hole with clubs."

"Where would we get a ferret?" I demanded. "And besides, we'd have to have somebody handle the ferret.

I don't want to be partly responsible for a ferret getting loose in our neighborhood."

"Well, I've got some rats," said Jim, with pride, "and I want to find some sporty way of dealing with them."

"I tell you," I cried, "we'll drown them out. Why didn't I think of it sooner? Of course, drown them out. How many holes have they got?"

"Two," said Jim. "One under the corner of the garage and another at the back. We can block one hole up and turn the hose into the other and they've got to come out."

"You've got it," I agreed. "I've often drowned rats out. They hate water."

And we went home a little early so as to deal with the rats before darkness came to their aid. Jimmie got his son's baseball bat and we brought the hose up from the cellar, where it had been stored for the winter. We turned on the water at the outside tap that had been turned off for fear of frost, and we proceeded to study the terrain.

Just under the south corner of the garage a hole about the size of a milk bottle led downward steeply. At the back of the garage a much smaller hole served as an emergency exit. Trust a rat for emergencies.

"It looks as if a whole army of rats used this front entrance," I said, as we examined the larger hole. "They probably hold meetings here. Maybe this is a public hall."

"They've got a great cave under there," said Jim. "I bet it's tunnelled into a regular apartment. An apartment with a concrete roof. The floor of the garage gives them an ideal bombproof shelter."

So we took sticks and gravel and cinders and filled up the smaller emergency exit at the back. We shoved all the stuff deep down, packing it in, so as to prevent any possibility of the rats digging out by that route.

Then we turned the hose on and into the larger hole I directed the stream while Jim limbered up with the baseball bat, in readiness.

"You've got to be ready for fast work, Jim," I cautioned him, "because when they come they may come all in a bunch."

"Don't fret," said Jim, "I can hit with this bat faster than they can fight their way past that stream."

And indeed it was a dandy stream, because in winter the water pressure is good. No other hose owners are watering any lawns. A powerful jet of water bored into the hole and we could hear it gurgling and swishing deep in the dark cavern of the rats.

"They may come any minute," I warned.

And Jimmie stood poised and tense.

"What do you suppose is going on down there?" I chuckled, as the water gushed. "I bet there's a commotion."

"They were likely asleep," said Jim, "and about now they are getting anxious. This is no ordinary rainstorm."

"Heh, heh, heh," I laughed, and squatted down to aim the icy water deeper and more vicious.

"They probably have galleries and upper levels," said Jim, "into which they are already fighting their way. How long do you suppose it will take to flood 'em?"

"Well, there's probably quite a large space," I submitted, "counting all the rooms and galleries. It may take several minutes. The earth is soft under there and will naturally soak up quite a lot of water."

"It's sand under there," said Jim. "It sure will soak it up. This may take half an hour or more."

"Relax," I said, seeing Jim still poised with the bat. "Take a look around the back at that escape hole and see there is no sign of anything being tampered with."

Jim skipped around to the back and returned eagerly to report that the hole was thoroughly stopped.

Still the water from the hose hissed and bored into the hole, which consumed it without any sign of filling. No sound of gurgling came from below any more though I put my ear down.

Jim made several trips around to the rear: to see that the exit was properly secure. It was chilly work holding the hose, and when I suggested Jimmie take a turn at running the water in, he said I would be too cramped to do a proper job of execution in case the rats came out.

"Look What You Did!"

And suddenly there was a most extraordinary result. With a loud crash, something inside the garage fell. We could hear the car inside bump heavily against the front doors of the garage, and bulge them outward.

"The floor," bellowed Jimmie, "the cement floor, you sap!"

I ceased firing with the hose and ran around to the front of the garage with Jimmie. Very carefully, Jim unlatched the bulging doors, and when he opened them, there was his car sunk down on its left rear wheel, its front end high in the air, one-half of the cement floor of the garage having collapsed into a huge dark hole in the ground.

"Look what you did," shouted Jim.

"The rats did it, not me," I retorted hotly.

"That water ate away the sand," accused Jim.

"The rats had dug the hole," I countered. "The whole foundation of your garage was honeycombed with rat tunnels."

"It would have held forever, if you hadn't bored in there with that hose," concluded Jim. "You and your drowning out methods."

It was a mess, all right. The car was tipped down at least three feet on its rear end, and securely wedged into the hole.

"Did you see any rats?" I inquired, incidentally.

"I certainly didn't," said Jim.

"Well," I assured, "I bet you're rid of them. That's what I undertook to do, at your own request—rid you of the rats."

"A fine mess," said Jim.

"Now you can put a proper foundation under your garage," I pointed out, "and never be troubled with rats again."

"Any child would have known," mutered Jim, "that you can't run a hose for 20 minutes into sand . . ."

"Look, Jim," I interrupted, "did you or did you not wish to be rid of the rats? Well you're rid of them."

So Jim phoned for the garage man to come with his derrick and hoist out the car. And the garage man's brother-in-law was in the cement business; and before supper, the whole situation was well in hand.

And Jimmie is rid of rats.

Summer Blues

June 20, 1940

"Well," said Jimmie Frise, "it can't be put off any longer."

"What can't?" I inquired.

"Locating a summer cottage," said Jim. "I've been stalling it off for weeks, and now my family is about ready to go away for the summer. But where?"

"You should have no trouble," I assured him. "Up near our place, there must be a dozen attractive summer homes for rent this year. You just decide on a price you want to pay and then take the first one that fits."

"Oh, is that so?" asked Jim. "I see you have never rented a cottage."

"No," I admitted. "We still have the one I was raised in from childhood, and then I married into another one."

"Well, that should break the monotony to some extent," said Jim.

"How do you mean?" I asked indignantly.

"I can't imagine anything more deadly than owning a

... *Out the back, over the*
rocks we ran, noses into the
breeze.

summer cottage," said Jim. "You never get rid of it. You live in it generation after generation. It grows aged and infirm, but you cling to it grimly. Every tree, every stone, every berry bush becomes familiar to you, and you watch the bushes and trees changing with the years, but no new ones ever come. You see the same people, the old ones aging, the young ones growing up to fulfil your worst expectations. The shingles curl, the veranda posts become decayed and punky. Floor boards grow weak and threaten always to collapse. But you cling to it still. No matter how your condition may alter in business or society, you still stick to the summer cottage. At last, when you can't bear it any longer, you rent it."

"Oh, come, come," I said.

"In all my years of exploring the summer cottage situation in this part of the world," said Jim, "I have never seen a new summer cottage. All summer cottages are old. There must have been a terrific cottage building boom about 1900."

"Where have you done most of your looking for summer cottages?" I demanded.

"All over," said Jim. "But I don't expect anything different. I'll go out this week-end and drive around the old familiar summer resorts, Lake Simcoe, Balsam Lake, Muskoka. And I'll end up by renting, as usual, some mouse-infested, dead-leaf-filled, musty, mouldy, hand-me-down old fire-trap of a cottage, and at least we will be better off than those who own cottages and are condemned to suffer the same one year after year."

"Have you asked your friends?" I inquired.

"You can't tell by them," said Jim. "Comfortably furnished cottage, they say, in select neighborhood, bathing, two rowboats. That's the last one I heard about. And when I got there, it was comfortable, in so far as it had chairs to sit on, though somewhat warped. There was bathing, if you wanted to sprain your ankle by wading amongst slimy boulders. There were two rowboats, but both of them were sunk in the ramshackle boathouse which the ice had all but washed away."

"You are just pessimistic," I assured Jim. "There are hundreds of delightful cottages."

Pictures of Lord Roberts

"There were funny old cracked dishes, and pictures of Lord Roberts tacked to the walls," went on Jim gloomily. "And another picture of Queen Victoria, sitting, with King Edward, then the Prince of Wales, standing stoutly behind her chair. The mirrors in the different rooms made your face look comic."

"How much was it?" I asked.

"For the season, $150," said Jim.

"Very reasonable," I said. "Lots of the better-class summer cottages cost from $600 to $1,000 for the two months. But I see you have a prejudice in this matter. You start out with the fatalistic feeling that you will be disappointed. I'd be glad to help you find a cottage. I am lucky, because I am cheerful. I expect to be pleased. And I am. It always works."

"You might make a big success," suggested Jim, "going about solving problems for pessimistic people. A professional. Like a water diviner."

"I still believe," I said, "that if you go expecting to be pleased you are much more likely to find what you want than if you go expecting to be disappointed."

"Let's look at an agent's list and see if there are any cottages," suggested Jim, working away at his drawing board. So I procured a list of summer cottages for rent. Small ones, large ones, from $10 a week to $500 a month. Some with nothing but a beautiful vista. Others with hot and cold running water, double garage, sleeping quarters over the boat-house, motor launch if desired, and so forth.

"How would $100 a month catch you?" I asked Jim.

"Too high," said Jim. "Let's hear something around $50 a month."

"You mustn't forget," I pointed out, "that the two months' rent is all the owner gets for the whole year."

"After paying $900 for it in the reign of King Edward," said Jim, "and then raising all his own family there and three lots of grandchildren until it is entirely worn out from use, how much return should a man expect from his investment in a summer cottage?"

"There is the sentimental value," I argued.

"What have you got there at $50 a month?" asked Jim.

I read down the list, and came to three at $50 a month. One was near the city, only 11 miles out.

"Probably an abandoned chicken ranch," said Jim.

The next one was at Lake Simcoe.

"Probably the one we were in last season," muttered Jim.

The third one was in Muskoka, beautifully situated, tastefully furnished, most exclusive neighborhood, boating, bathing, fishing. Only careful tenant need apply.

"Ha, ha," said Jimmie, "Careful not to step too heavy."

"Jim," I said, "I like the sound of that one. Tastefully furnished."

"Faded Chinese lanterns hanging from the rough board ceiling of the living-room," sneered Jim.

"Beautifully situated," I read.

"In a bed of poison ivy," suggested Jim.

"Somehow," I said, "this one gives me a hunch. I'd be glad to run up with you and lend you my good luck."

Before McKinley Was Shot

So we called up the telephone of the Toronto gentleman who was offering the cottage for rent, and agreed to meet him in the Muskoka village on Saturday and he would guide us in to see it. A lovely drive up Yonge St., with that happy early-season feeling, when the roads seem to sing under your wheels and none of the trees are faded or dusty.

We met the gentleman in the village and he got in our car and guided us down roads that got narrower and wilder until we came out on the lake.

"It's just a short walk in from here," said the gentleman. "We have always resisted any idea of running the road any farther than this. I don't want any motor traffic whizzing past my sylvan retreat. Don't you think so?"

"There wouldn't be much whizzing on this road," said Jim.

We walked for 10 or 15 minutes along paths, along the beach, climbing over rocks and driftwood and pushing through thickets.

"Here we are," cried the gentleman.

There were six cottages in a row, all closely spaced beside one another. They were rather aged.

"Which one?" asked Jim, glumly.

"The fourth one," said the gentleman gaily. "Ah, I hate to let it go, you can have no idea what this little place means to my family! But with the girls all grown up— and so forth."

We walked along the rocks in front of the row and stepped on to the faded veranda of the fourth cottage. You could step from the veranda of one to the veranda of the others.

"With all the room in Muskoka," said Jim, "why do they build the cottages in huddles like this?"

"Ah, you have no idea what lovely neighbors these are," said the gentleman. "The bonfires at night, the singing, the weiner roasts. It's just a little community. The women folk prefer this to lonely cottages spaced far apart. We feel sorry for those people who own islands. One lonely cottage on an island. Don't you think?"

We examined the cottage. The veranda posts were still firm. But the railing had been patched. There were broad stains under the roof, where leaks occurred. The screens were gray and had holes. When the gentleman opened the door, having considerable difficulty with the key, the familiar cottage smell smote us. Into the dark interior we stepped, and the gentleman walked over and drew a blind a little way. How thoroughly the ladies close up a cottage, little caring what a desolate view is to meet the eye in the summer to come! Wash tubs upside down on the living-room floor. Mattresses suspended on wire clothes lines, mice nests on the chair, for always one cushion is forgotten at the last minute.

"Stuffy, isn't it?" said the gentleman. "But a cottage always smells stuffy after being closed all winter."

The floor was littered with leaves, and somebody else will have to figure how those leaves get in.

Jim stepped gingerly and doubtfully from room to room.

"Ah," said he, pointing to a picture of Lord Roberts in scarlet tunic tacked to a bedroom wall.

Nice people had lived in this cottage. There were old-

213

fashioned things tacked to the walls, and no matter how faded they had become, nice people had been too in love with the years that had gone to tear them down. There were frayed palm fans scrawled with names. Picture postcards, dim with age. Funny looking wall vases with Muskoka painted on them. Bulrushes that must have been sprayed upon that wall before McKinley was shot.

There were home-made cabinets in the dining room and kitchen. The chairs around the table were all odd. There was a high chair, specially faded and worn.

A mouse skittered across the kitchen.

"Dear, dear, the first mouse I ever saw in here," said the gentleman.

"What is that other smell?" asked Jim.

And there was indeed another smell.

A Wonderful Philosophy

"This Muskoka breeze will soon rid the cottage of that stuffy air," said the gentleman. "Now come around here to the back, and I'll show you the best part of the whole place. It is the envy of all your neighbors. A stone cellar! Yes, sir, a solid stone cellar, not large, you understand, but what a convenience, for the women. It keeps food perfectly. No matter how often the supply boats fails to come, no matter how the cows of the man who supplies the milk may stray, you can count on this cellar to keep a good supply of perishable food in perfect condition.

We went under the cottage at the back. There was a dark cavern, in which stones cemented together formed a wall with a wooden door in it. The door was ajar.

The gentleman went first, Jim followed. I brought up the rear.

The gentleman scratched a match. There were wild shouts, yells and a stampede, I leading. And the dense and brand new odor of skunk billowed out past us no matter how fast we travelled.

Out the back, over the rocks, down to the bouldery shore, we ran, noses into the breeze.

"Gentlemen," gasped our guide. "How unfortunate! I hope you escaped."

"We can't tell for a while yet," said Jim.

"Perhaps if we waited a little while the animal would go away, and I could show you more fully . . ."

"Is this the bathing beach?" asked Jim.

"There is a good beach about half a mile down the shore," said the gentleman. "Just a nice walk."

"I'm afraid," said Jim, "that I must have a beach right in front of my cottage. That is one thing my family insists on."

"In that case—" said the gentleman.

So we went up and locked the doors very softly and carefully while we waited in the breeze. We drove him back to the village and Jim and I went home in the evening.

We were conscious of a faint odor, our cigarettes tasted queer, and the attendants at the gas station at Orillia looked at us oddly. But you soon get used to anything. Especially if you are a summer cottage owner.

"Well," said Jim, "you didn't divine a skunk when you divined that cottage for me!"

"The skunk," I said, "saved you from accepting the cottage. You might have taken the cottage in sheer boredom if there hadn't been that skunk. I am lucky. My luck even provides skunks."

"You have a wonderful philosophy," admitted Jim.

"How would you like to drive home down around the other side of Lake Simcoe?" I asked, "and we could look over some of the cottage resorts in passing."

"No," said Jim, "I have been through all this before. It's just the same old thing. At last, in desperation, we'll take a cottage by mail or long distance telephone. And when we get there, it will be painted gray, with posts having 1904 carved under them, and there will be a swamp in front and a big empty stony field behind, and the man who delivers the ice will be very intemperate and everybody on the point will be nervous of him. And the mosquitoes will be bad until the 20th of July, and in August the family will lie around reading last year's magazines, getting crankier and crankier and wanting to come home to the city."

"Jim," I accused, "you are a complete pessimist."

"No," said Jim. "I'm just an average Canadian."

A Quiet Evening With Walton

June 19, 1937

"How'd you like," asked Jimmie Frise, "to come up to Andy's with me to-night?"

"Aw, Jim," I said, "you go. But I don't get along with Andy, you know that. He wants to talk about strikes."

"I've got to go," said Jim. "And I said I'd bring you."

"He's a rich guy," I protested. "And all he wants to do is get a couple of poor birds at his mercy and talk about Communists."

"He's very interested in you," stated Jim. "He thinks you have the makings of a serious writer if you'd only meet the right people and get some sound ideas."

"Now I won't go," I assured him. "I've got along all right so far without any sound ideas and I don't intend to start at my age."

"Slowly and methodically we lifted our
feet and put them down. . . . . A car horn
tooted at us. . . . A group of young
people hailed us. . . . Several small dogs
yipped at our heels. . . ."

217

"If you would only chum up with some of the important people," declared Jim, "you might get somewhere. Instead of spending your life with any old tramp so long as he is a fisherman. . . ."

"Jim," I protested, "I won't have you calling yourself a tramp. Not in my presence, anyway. You may be only a cartoonist, but if you had mingled with the right people and got some sound ideas, you might easily have been a great artist."

"Now don't get sarcastic," said Jim. "Andy has been telephoning me now for about six months, inviting me up to his place. I've been ducking and dodging but yesterday he got me and said 'All right, what night can you come?' And there he had me."

"I wish people would stick to a certain night when they invite you," I agreed. "Then you can say you have an engagement for that night. But this business of saying 'what night will you come?' is a lousy trick."

"It sure is," said Jim. And that's where we stand. I said I'd go to-night."

"Well, Jim," I said happily, "tell Andy I'm sorry I had an engagement for to-night."

"Andy's a good guy, even if he is rich," said Jim. "I wish you'd get to know him better. He could be a lot of use to you."

"I don't want any friends to be of use to me," I informed him. "I think that is the trouble with Andy. I have the feeling the only people he wants to know are ones that will be of use to him. He probably has the feeling that he owes it to society to get to know some newspapermen and fill them up with his ideas about Communists and things."

"He's got some swell English guns," said Jim.

"Puh," said I.

"He's got one of the most interesting sporting libraries in Canada," pursued Jim.

"Puh," I repeated.

"Just lately," said Jim, "he got a shipment of old books from a sale in England and in it is a copy of the second edition of the Compleat Angler."

The Rare Edition

"Oh, yeah?" I laughed. "Second edition, eh? Do you know how much Andy would have to pay for that?"

"He told me he paid a hundred and ten pounds," said Jim, quietly. "Five hundred and fifty dollars."

"Jim." I said after a moment, "you're not fooling, are you?"

"I'm just telling you what Andy told me," said Jim. "Second edition. Is that rare?"

"Rare?" I shouted. "Rare? Second edition of the Compleat Angler, you dummy? Why, Walton rewrote the book entirely for the second edition, and its a duodecimo, with ten engraved plates of fish, and there are original sheets of the Angler's Song, and it's rarer than the first edition. . . . Jimmie, maybe Walton actually handled this copy, himself, at the printers . . ."

"Well, if you think so much of it," said Jim, "why don't you come up and see it?"

"Come up and see it?" I cried. "Who can stop me? Good old Andy. Now, there's a true Canadian for you. Using his wealth to obtain for Canada some of the worth-while treasures."

"I'll let him know you are coming," said Jim cheerfully.

And I went home early to spend a little while looking at my poor half-dozen editions of Walton, none of them worth ten dollars or dating farther than 1823, but very friendly in the hand, none the less. By merely touching these noble old books, I prepared my mood for the great honor I was to be accorded in holding in my very hands a copy of the Second Edition.

Jimmie picked me up early to drive to Andy's, who lives in one of those fashionable neighborhoods above Eglinton Ave. on the fringe of the country.

We drove through districts that had not even been districts the last time I was up this way, depression or no depression. Through handsome streets of spacious homes set side-ways to the street instead of endways, which was the old-fashioned and more economical method.

"Here's Andy's," said Jim, slowing and eyeing a fine colonial red brick home with green shutters, the kind that are never shut. "Last time I was here, there were no houses on either side."

"This city is sure growing," I confessed.

We parked and strolled up the walk.

"Andy said," remarked Jim, "that he had to drive his wife over to Yonge St. and everybody's out, so just walk in."

"Let's sit on the veranda," I offered. "I don't care about walking into people's homes."

"Don't be lower class," laughed Jim, trying the front door. "Be modern. Be smart. Walk right in."

However, the door was locked.

"I didn't think Andy was the kind to leave any doors open," I said.

"He said walk right in," said Jim, "and make ourselves at home. I guess it's the side door."

We went around the side drive into Andy's very handsome garden. Jim tried the side door and a small back door that led into a sort of basement recreation room, by the look of it.

"H'm," said Jim, they being all securely locked.

So we sat on a bench and watched the gentleman next door bent over his flower bed, weeding and forking.

"They're After Us"

I recited in a low voice for Jimmie some of the lovelier passages of Walton, the one beginning "nevertheless, here I must part with you; here in this now sad place, where I was so happy as first to meet you." And I gave him the famous passage "and we having still a mile to Tottenham High-Cross, I will, as we walk towards it in the cool shade of this sweet honeysuckle hedge, mention to you some of the thoughts and joys that have possessed. . . ."

But you know Walton. Anyway, a little time passed and Jim got up and walked out the drive to look for Andy.

"You might as well be inside, looking at that old book," said Jim, "as moaning about it out here."

He tried the side and little back doors again, and then pushed at a casement window in the cellar room. It gave.

"Ah," said Jim, "I'll crawl through and open the door for you."

"Ah," said I, rising, for my hands were aching for that old book, and I went and stood at the side door, while Jim vanished trhough the window.

I heard a dreadful shriek. I heard Jim's voice loudly speaking. I heard the thud of steps and Jim burst out the door.

"What the . . ." I demanded.

"An old lady," said Jim breathlessly. "An old lady. She nearly scared me to death."

"Well, tell her who you are." I commanded.

"I tried to tell her Andy said to walk in," said Jim. "But she just let out a shriek and ran down the hall. Just a minute."

Jim hurried to the edge and called across to the gentleman gardening next door.

"Pardon me, sir," said Jim, "but this is where Mr. Andy Daleberry lives, isn't it?"

"No," said the gentleman. "Mr. Daleberry lives one block further. . . ."

But I was already half way down the drive heading for the car. Jim hastened after me.

"Jim," I snarled, "she's likely called the police."

"We can explain," said Jim, hurriedly starting the engine.

"I'm sick and tired of explaining," I declared.

I glanced back and saw a small dark car come curving wildly around the corner at the end of the street.

"There's the police radio car now," I cried. "Stay still! Explain!"

But Jim had the car slightly in motion at that instant, and such is the ancient fear in the human heart, the first instinct is always to run. And with a rush and a roar, Jim leaped his car into high.

"I'll shake them in a couple of blocks," gasped Jim. "They'll have to stop at the house for a second. . . ."

"Jim, this is a mistake," I groaned.

"Watch me," said Jim tensely.

And he slewed around a corner, raced a block, turned another corner, and twisting and doubling back he made his way southward through handsome streets towards Eglinton Ave., that great east and west artery across the top of the city.

I sat facing back, watching anxiously for the police car. I saw it speed past one intersection just as we vanished around the turn, a full block south.

"Jim," I cried, "they're after us. What'll we say now, if they catch us?"

"They'll not catch us," muttered Jim. "Here's Eglinton. We'll lose ourselves quietly in the traffic."

But the traffic was thicker, this fine June evening, than could be easily entered. And it was somewhat congested, right at the foot of the block we approached it by, due to the fact that two or three dozen of those marathon runners, in their shorts and jerseys, were at that very moment strung along, running with chins high and arms bent up, westward along the highway.

"Quick," hissed Jim, starting to tear off his coat.

"What?" I begged.

"Take off your clothes," yelled Jim, already removing his shirt. "The cops'll be around that last corner in a jiffy. They can't miss this car. Quick."

"What?" I repeated.

"We're runners, see?" cried Jim.

It was only a couple of sweeps and a swipe for me to remove my clothes.

"Stuff them in the compartment behind the seat," Jim ordered.

We jammed our clothes out of sight.

"Come on," snapped he, opening the car door and crouching. "Allright, now head up, arms bent high. Let's go!"

And ducking around two or three cars waiting to turn into Eglinton Ave., Jim and I sprinted out and joined the parade of marathon runners. Fortunately, they were strung out, in groups and pairs and singles, and Jim and I, neck and neck, formed only one unit in the long and straggling parade.

"How far," I puffed, "do we go?"

"We'll have to go," puffed Jim, "all the way home."

"But Jim," I panted, "we can't run five miles."

"Take it easy," said Jim. "We don't have to win this race. All we got to do is keep in it."

"Jim," I gasped, "we'll have to rest pretty soon."

"Can't rest," whuffed Jim. "In these underclothes. Long as we are running it's proper. Once we stop it's indecent."

"Oooooh," I said, slackening.

So we slackened, and runner after runner went by us, with long, easy legs, many of them turning a brief surprised glance at us as they passed.

Slower and slower our feet went, as we passed Dufferin St. and saw ahead in the sunset the towering tops of the packing houses; and our socks worked down over our shoes and our eyes bulged and our lungs ached but we slowly and methodically lifted them and put them down, while at length no more runners passed us in the growing twilight and the lights came on and still down past the packing houses we panted and plodded.

A couple of curious motor cars slowed and followed us short distances. Some car horns were tooted at us. A few groups of young summer people on street corners hailed us with modernistic cheers. Several small dogs yipped at our heels. But by now we could cut down the quieter streets and the streets we knew as nigh unto home. And with a last, leaden terrible quarter mile, we came down a lane and into Jim's yard and there we fell.

"Got to get inside," said Jim, sitting up and gulping air. "Phone police."

"What for?" I gasped.

But Jim staggered up and, much as I loved that soft green sod, I followed him. He sat by the phone a couple of minutes until his breath grew more normal. And then he dialled the phone.

"Police?" said Jim, angrily. "Say, my car has been stolen from in front of my house. Frise is the name."

And he gave his address and there was some waiting until they switched him to another police station.

"Yes," Jim shouted hotly. "Stolen from right in front here."

Pause.

"You've been phoning me? Here? Oh," said Jim, "I've been out in the garden watering. I guess I couldn't hear the phone for the hose. You've got the car? Good! Splendid! Where is it? On Eglinton, eh? Is it damaged?"

Another pause.

"Clothes," cried Jim. "Behind the back seat? Oh, those are our fishing clothes. Sure. My friend and I always keep a suit of old clothes in the car for going fishing."

"Now that's kind of you," said Jim.

He hung up.

"They're bringing the car here," said Jim. "Beat it home and get some clothes on."

Which I did, and when the police arrived, Jim and I were sitting on his veranda and I was reciting some more swell bits out of Walton, the one about "the salmon is accounted the King of freshwater fish; and is ever bred in rivers relating to the sea."

And we thanked the police most warmly for the way they looked after stodgy old book-lovers like us.